YOGA
&SEX

YOGA & SEX

by PANDIT SHIV SHARMA
KAILASH NATH SHARMA

HARRAP LONDON

First published in Great Britain 1973
by GEORGE G. HARRAP & CO. LTD
182–184 High Holborn, London WC1V 7AX

© *Sharma & Sharma* 1973

ISBN 0 245 50945 3

*Composed in Goudy Old Style type and printed
by Redwood Press Limited, London and Trowbridge
Made in Great Britain*

Contents

Authors' Note

Some portions of this book have been written singly and some jointly by the authors. This explains the use of the first person singular in some places and of the first person plural in others where it has been considered desirable to address the readers directly.

Introduction

No gift is greater than the gift of knowledge. The knowledge of the practice of Yoga is perhaps the greatest of them all. It is not difficult to acquire at the level you and I can practise it. Once you have this knowledge you will find that Yoga is neither a bed of nails, nor a mass of tangled hair, nor unattainably 'Eastern'. It is a bed of roses, a source of radiant joy and of scintillating health. Yoga will not only add years to your life, but life to your years.

The demonstrable benefits which Yoga confers on those who practise it have made this subject popular in both East and West. At this stage it is desirable that an exposition of the potential contribution of Yoga to the health and integrity of the sex urge, and the improved performance of the sex act, should be made available to the general reader.

We are living through an era of sexual emancipation characterized by a profusion of candid literature on sex unknown during the Victorian era. It is therefore indeed surprising that, when the number of books on the subjects of both Yoga and sex should be continuing to flood the market, no authentic treatise has been available revealing the close and elevating relationship which exists between these two techniques. I hope that *Yoga and Sex* will not only fill this gap, but will bring knowledge, happiness and joy to all of you who read it. Yoga, in the sense it is described here, is a science and not a cult. In order to enjoy its benefits, therefore, I do not have to ask you to have faith in it. It is enough to practise it. The benefits of the effects of faith are believed to transcend the realm of reason and intelligence. The soundness of the effects of Yoga is universal. A person having no faith in Yoga as a cult will receive identical benefits through the practice of Yoga as will the ardent believer, just as a non-believer in the nutritional value of food receives the same sustenance from what he eats as the dietitian who understands the principle of nutrition. Negatively, the analogy can be extended to arsenic which will kill both the believer and the non-believer in the action of the drug.

The sages, saints and seers of ancient India who dealt with sex merely described the science of sex. They did not preach it. The great sage Vatsyayana specifically underlines this attitude in his monumental work *Kama Sutra*, when he states that the descriptions of the properties of dog's meat given by Charaka do not imply that Charaka himself ate dog's meat. Therefore Vatsyayana's description of postures relating to sexual intercourse, or his narrations of the various perversions prevalent in certain countries during that time, should not be taken to mean that he himself indulged in these practices. Knowledge was sacrosanct and had to be imparted in full without any interference with its totality.

Hatha Yoga is a science. Yoga as a whole may be a combination of science and philosophy, but it is certainly not a religion. Yet although this book is concerned with the clinical use of Yoga, it is impossible to ignore its spiritual influence. As you will see later, Yoga elevates and spiritualizes sex itself. The added ecstasy of the spirituality attained through Yoga much enhances the physical thrill of sex. The orgasmic explosion is intensified and post-coital tranquillity acquires an element of the divine.

The practice of Hatha Yoga recognizes the claim of facts and gives them preference over non-factual conventions of religion and custom. The facts of sex are consistent from man to man, race to race, and country to country, although customs and conventions are very different. If a popular Western figure is carrying on affairs with a large number of women and holds them as his willing slaves in the realm of extra-marital relationships he is, in essence, a replica of the oriental potentate possessing a large number of women in his harem. But the latter lives well within his religion and customs, while the former violates (particularly if he is married) his religious and social conventions. Yet the physician looks only at the sexual act, its frequency and intensity and its psychosomatic repercussions on the individual. How this sort of life affects the patient is more important to the physician than the question of the propriety of his behaviour. The prescription of Yoga in these cases is more clinical than spiritual, even if the spiritual contribution of Yoga can never be completely excluded.

Yoga will demonstrate to you convincingly that good can beat evil and that there is good and bad sex, the former leading to complete joy and exhilaration, and to sound, relaxed and lasting physical and mental health. Short of 'divine' ecstasy (if such a phenomenon exists) which is claimed to have been experienced by mystics, saints and prophets, a judicious understanding and practice of Yoga and sex takes you as near the divine ecstasy as a normal human being can achieve.

I hope this book will be found entertaining since entertainment is an inherent characteristic of sex. If in addition it gives you knowledge it will bring a deep abiding joy into your life, for a satisfying and integrated life, inclusive of sex, is inherent in Yoga.

Roman spelling has been deliberately used for the Sanskrit words to enable the reader to pick up their pronunciation with ease and passable accuracy.

Yoga-Sex Relationship

There is no sexual organ more important than the human mind, no physical and mental experience or 9 sensation-complex more ecstatic and blissful than an ideal and complete sexual union between two truly loving partners. There are no anaphrodisiacs, dampeners or desexualizers worse than ignorance, anxiety and fear regarding the quality and effectiveness of one's performance of the sex act. There is no sexual tonic greater than a partner whose total physical and psychic personality reflects, embodies, meets and satisfies your demands, tastes, desires and notions of attractiveness, love, warmth and richness, depth, spontaneity and mutuality of response. There is no aphrodisiac and sex reconditioner more rewarding or far-reaching than Yoga.

Again, this ecstasy is not that rare mystic experience claimed by saints and prophets. Some of the claimants of 'divine' experiences describe this mystic religious bliss as a permanent and continuing state of orgasmal ecstasy! This is unlikely, however, to be the aim of the general reader. Even if it were possible through some kind of austerity and stratagem to turn the peak of orgasm into an eternal and limitless plateau, it should not be forgotten that a plateau of a uniform and unchanging feeling usually involves a great deal of boredom. The statements made here are addressed exclusively to men and women whose sense perceptions or perceptual experiences do not transcend the world of common and natural physical and psychic phenomena.

It may be asked how these two subjects, sex and Yoga, can be bracketed together in view of the general belief that the ideals and practices of sex are basically antagonistic to those of Yoga, and vice-versa, and that the pursuit of one tends to lead to the abandonment of the other. The *Ashtanga* (octopartite) Yoga has, for its ideals, the eight traditional categories of Yogic discipline, namely 1 *Yama* (eight self-controls); 2 *Niyama* (eight additional self-restraints); 3 *Asanas* (Yogic postures); 4 *Prana-*

yama (Yogic-breath culture); 5 *Pratyahara* (withdrawal of sense organs from their objects); 6 *Dharana* (steadying the mind); 7 *Dhyana* (Yogic meditation); and 8 *Samadhi* (total Yogic abstraction). These are disciplines which do not go together with the practice of sex. The first category of these, *Yama*, insists, among other controls, on the practice of celibacy—an apparent antithesis of sexual activity—as an essential discipline to be practised by the Yogi.

People often seem to reserve a degree of reverence for Yoga which is lacking in their attitude to sex. So it may seem to appear that the practices of Yoga and sex can only co-exist, but cannot co-ordinate, with each other. Even in Western countries where so much literature is available on each of these subjects, their co-ordination is not discussed.

The complete Yogic discipline with its rigidity and austerity is mainly the domain of the recluse who, withdrawing from the intimacies, attractions and distractions of worldly life, has chosen the path of renunciation, asceticism and transcendentalism. This book is not written for such a person.

It is now a widely demonstrated and proven fact that normal men and women, while giving full and effective attention to their work routine and family life, can adopt the practice of Yoga with great physical and mental benefit to themselves and a welcome improvement in all aspects of their lives, including their sexual activities. Yoga builds up human health and resistance whether the practitioner uses it for one pursuit or for another. Yoga helps you rule over sex, instead of allowing sex to rule you. *You* master your emotions and play with them as you like instead of these emotions mastering and playing with you. This cannot be said of drugs, alcohol, hormonal injections and tranquillizers. Yoga streamlines sex behaviourally, emotionally and spiritually.

11

Yoga puts sex into perspective and the mind which is invigorated by Yoga is not warped by sex but is free from sexual obsession. With Yoga you do not push unpleasant thoughts into the subconscious but instead you liberate them. You consciously and effectively overcome the insatiable desire for variety, novelty and discovery in sex which can drive an individual from one partner to another without satisfaction, and which in its most extreme form creates sexual maniacs.

When self-control is difficult it creates resentment and frustration and when it is made easy it is elevating and rewarding. Both Yoga and healthy sexual activity invariably relax and invigorate mind and body. An entire day may be more rewarding after morning sex. It can clear rather than cloud the mind. This contribution of sex to your success is almost identical with that of Yoga.

Marriage makes enormous demands on the partners who often break down in the absence of physical, mental and temperamental adjustments. Yoga softens the background of neurosis. This the psychiatrist may find hard to accept for to him the catharsis and purging the subconscious of unknown repressions is the only way out. Perhaps he will find it difficult to agree that the mind can be untwisted by merely twisting the body, and yet it is true the Asanas (Yogic postures) do simultaneously affect both the mind and the body for the better. (This aspect of Yoga has been explained in my earlier work *Yoga Against Spinal Pain** in the chapter 'The Rationale of Yoga'.)

Indolence and sloth are the basic enemies of sexual efficiency as they retard every physical and mental discipline, and discipline is the basis of every

* Published in Great Britain by Harrap Books 1972 and in the US under the title of *Yoga for Backaches* by Cornerstone Library.

type of efficiency including that in sex. Again, Yoga is one way in which you can conquer indolence and sloth. The most important contribution of Yoga to the entire range of life, including sex, is that it converts stress into a challenge. Therefore for a true practitioner of Yoga it ceases to be important to avoid stress since this can be converted into a challenge and the result is more effective than any achieved by use of an artificial sexual tonic.

The word 'Yoga' is derived from the Sanskrit root *Yuj*—to join. The same root *Yuj* in *Samyojanam* means sexual intercourse. This sharing of derivations is, I think, both interesting and relevant.

Yoga's contribution to the mind improves the mind's contribution to sex. Yoga makes self-control easy and at the same time, with the flexibility and steadiness of Yoga behind you, you can switch on to sex without anxiety.

Both Yoga and sex are psychosomatic techniques. Both are subject to dominance of physical phenomena at one time (Asanas, coitus) and, as in the case of *Dhyana* (meditation) or pure love, of spiritual elements at another. The exalted love in sex stands for everything that Yoga stands for— oneness, truth and spirituality. Secretiveness and lies in sexual matters will end only in hypocrisy, and once truthfulness is undermined the entire fabric of trust is destroyed.

The unsuspected and unrecognized relationship between Yoga and sex is an intimate one. They have many things in common and both the Yogic and the sexual exercises, when intelligently conducted and ideally performed, lead to longevity, alertness, radiant health, contentment, serenity and tranquillity. Both lead to an abatement of anger, irritability, unsociability, cruelty and criminality. Most sexual crimes are committed by people who could not find a normal outlet for their sex urge and many

13

anti-social crimes, including non-sexual activities such as petty larceny, arson and other felonies, are committed by people suffering from sexual frustration. Both Yoga and sexual satisfaction promote tolerance and forgiveness, enrich the emotional life and promote an appreciation of truth and beauty. Both kill hate and promote love. Both benefit the body through the agency of the mind and, finally, nothing is as effectively conducive to resolving tension, both physical and mental, as the intelligent exercise of Yoga and sex.

Social, Cultural and Spiritual Aspects of Yoga and Sex

People generally attribute to sex the two functions of procreation and recreation. Having contained it within these two exclusive fields of activity, they close all other avenues of expectation. But sex offers much more than the limited ecstasy of orgasm and the satisfaction of perpetuation of the species. Orgasm can easily be achieved through masturbation, and procreation by means of artificial insemination. Sex is not mere lust, even if lust is sex. It transcends the two major animal functions and enters the realm of the cultural and spiritual. When combined with Yoga, sex can accelerate progress towards cultural refinement and spiritual health.

Deep satisfaction tranquillizes and steadies the mind. Dissatisfaction disturbs and erodes it—sometimes slowly, sometimes violently. Every act that soothes and satisfies an individual without resulting in an adverse reaction later on, and which promotes feelings of love, consideration and solicitude, constitutes progress towards culture and spirituality.

Therefore a proper exercise of a healthy sex urge, viewed from a detached, scientific perspective, is not only compatible with higher social, cultural and spiritual goals, but is actually conducive to them. When practised with Yoga, sex can give you a feeling of sublime well-being which will permeate your entire body, mind and spirit. Its excellence, purity and permanence are ennobling and exhilarating.

The most intense enjoyment of sex is consistent with the best traditions of character and integrity, just as the most stringent celibacy can be associated with cruelty and callousness of inquisitorial proportions, for celibacy under duress, or because of anxiety or fear, is no celibacy at all.

There is a general impression among people that Yoga leads the practitioner to a higher and higher spiritual life, culminating in final salvation and beatitude. It is thought that the ancient seers of India were against one living the life of a family man or woman, a life in which work interests, love of sensual pleasures, affection for family and friends, desire for the gratification of the sex urge, maintenance of radiant health and the pursuit of these and similar objectives occupied an honoured place of legitimate importance.

It is true that the first practitioners of Yoga were, in most cases, saints and recluses. They realized the importance of a state of perfect and healthy psychosomatic harmony as a prerequisite to the successful pursuit of any important goal, be it spiritual, material or sexual. But it must be emphasized that Yoga, and especially Hatha Yoga, was never considered an end in itself, but as a means to an end. Yoga may be utilized with equal efficiency to fulfil objectives other than those pursued by its more ascetic exponents. Most people in Europe, as also in the East, are taking up Yoga not in search of spirituality, but of sound mental and physical health. They are neither interested in dropping their usual pursuits, nor in adopting severe austerities. Yoga is not a compulsion but a free choice for seekers after spiritual truth and materialists alike, and there is much in Yoga which will make the most worldly pursuits beatific and beautiful. The culture which gave Sage Patanjali's Yoga to the world also gave Sage Vatsyayana's *Kama Sutra*. And the various Kamasanas or sex postures from the simplest to the most complex bear an analogy to the Yogic postures described in the classics.

In apparently diverting Yoga from the spiritual to the sexual I am betraying neither East nor West, for Yoga continues to exert its spiritual influence under all conditions. The Eastern mystics go further —they associate the fulfilment of sex with the attainment of the spiritual goal itself. Apart from showing a general reluctance to condemn sex, the early Indians regarded it as an inescapable religious duty of the family man to produce a son, without whom the gates of Heaven were closed to his soul. The religious leaders gave their full attention to the worldly happiness of their people. The development of sexual efficiency was not merely a fundamental right, it was considered a necessary part of the education and culture of a Nagaraka, the urban dweller, to be fully conversant with the art and science of love and sex. He would be guilty of failing in his duty towards himself and society if he did not equip himself with this knowledge.

A sexually dissatisfied person is a sour person, often unsociable and prone to develop anti-social trends. In contrast a sexually satisfied man or woman often feels that he or she owes much to the world which gives them such intense happiness.

Conjugal fidelity is a highly desirable trait in a civilized individual. However, it should arise out of natural or deep love, for when accepted as an infliction it can be used against one's spouse. There are those who believe that by offering complete fidelity to their spouses they have established the right to take away all other happiness. The wife who keeps her virginity intact before marrying sometimes feels she is giving so much she has a right to take something back. That 'something' may add up to all the happiness life can give. There are wives too, technically faithful to their marriage vows, who will drive hard bargains with their husbands before submitting to love-making; and there are many non-spouses who, in voluntary abandon, take on the mantle of true lovers even when technically guilty in some eyes of fornication and adultery. It is hard to say whether in the interests of peace and happiness the choice should be the sour and bitter faithful, or the considerate and solicitous unfaithful.

Yoga offers no ready solutions to these situations, nor has it any remedies for eternal triangles. Depending on the traits of the individuals practising Yoga, it merely improves, in varying degrees, the neuro-muscular and psychosomatic machinery and promotes tolerance and forgiveness where anger and wrath may be; cheerfulness instead of despondency; alertness instead of weakness; love instead of hate.

Development, Anatomy and Physiology of Sex

A vast amount of literature has been published on the evolution, development, anatomy and physiology of sex. The studies made on the subject could justify a book to themselves, rather than just a few words. Sexual problems have increased in the modern world, outstripping studies and methods of treatment. Many problems remain seemingly insurmountable. The advent of civilization has placed

17

man in an extremely difficult situation with regard to the free exercise of his basic urges. More often than not he has to learn to inhibit normal urges in order to be accepted as a member of the community in which he lives. Nowhere are these repressions exercised more deeply than in the realm of sex. This results in a continual battle between the mind and the body, or, to put it more neurologically, between the brain and the spinal cord. The veterans of this battle are men and women wearing scars at physical and psychological levels manifested in various sexual neuroses.

This book cannot begin to discuss each and every facet of sexual maturation and sexual inadequacy, but we will briefly touch upon certain salient points which are of importance to the uninitiated, and even more important to the wrongly initiated, while confining the main discussion to the role of co-ordination of the mind and the nervous system in the sexual act.

To be able to accomplish the sex act satisfactorily it is essential that the body be fit enough to stand up to the exertion demanded by it, and that the mind be free of worries.

Muscle-building exercises may make a man look like Mr Universe, but they do not increase his endurance and capacity for the sex act. Worries and tensions can also prevent the desk-bound executive from doing full justice to his role as a sex partner. The art of relaxing physically and mentally, while simultaneously increasing endurance, is a target which can be reached through the practice of Yoga. At the same time, the self-control and discipline which become second nature to the practitioner of Yoga prevent over-indulgence or misuse of the acquired faculties.

It is common knowledge that the testes and ovaries are the specialized glands that manufacture

18

sperm and ova respectively in the male and female, and also produce hormones which are eventually responsible for the maleness or femaleness of the individual. The hormonal secretions of these primary sex organs are responsible for the development of organs that are essential for procreation. These are called the accessory sex organs—the vagina, the uterus and the fallopian tubes in the female, and the seminal vesicles, epididymis, prostate gland and penis in the male. But although sex and reproduction are closely related, they are not essential to each other. Equally, although each pair of individuals is equipped with the apparatus to bring about the chance of fertilization taking place, psychic, emotional, intellectual and physical factors play an extremely important role in bringing two people together.

The Nervous System and the Sex Act

In discussing the neurological control of the sex act, we have to remember the very important fact that the basic neural sex mechanisms of animals have been so greatly modified in man, and are so dominated by the higher brain centres, that past experiences, emotional factors, conditioning and learning, all play an increasingly important role in our sex lives. The classification of the human nervous system that we employ below to explain this aspect is arbitrary, but convenient for an easier understanding of the whole where each section dovetails into the other to produce the ultimate result. Malfunction of any one of them is liable to have an equally drastic effect on the sexual performance of the individual.

We are presenting the information as briefly as possible, realizing that while it is essential that you

19

should understand the importance of an intact and trouble-free nervous machinery as a prerequisite to a satisfying and rewarding sex life, you are concerned with an effective performance of your system, rather than with the hows and whys behind it. The main function of this book is to deal with the ways and means of rectifying such faults as may adversely affect the smooth functioning of this machine.

Basically, we can divide the nervous control of sex into three different parts:

(a) The somatic nervous system
(b) The spinal cord
(c) The autonomic nervous system

The Somatic Nervous System

The somatic nervous system deals with the reception and perception of impulses from the outside world and the reaction of the organism to them. No one can deny the significance of sight, sound, touch and smell in the initiation and performance of the sex act. Learning and conditioning can make any of these senses more important than the others as is evident from the studies of different civilizations. The power of reason and the capacity for emotion can, and do, further modify this response.

The Role of the Spinal Cord

The spinal cord, housed in the spinal or vertebral column, is the connecting pathway between the brain and the periphery of the body. Through it sensations are relayed to appropriate areas of the brain and the commands, delivered by the brain, are carried to the proper organ, gland or muscle. The combination of an incoming sensory root, and outgoing motor root, and a connecting link between the two, is called a reflex arc. This is the simplest of the neural mechanisms. In man a number of such reflexes, though capable of working autonomously, are under the inhibitory and excitatory control of the higher brain centres.

The understanding of this basic spinal reflex and its modification by the brain is important since disharmony between these two is one of the commonest causes of sexual maladjustment. In lower mammals, the sexual act is a pure spinal reflex unencumbered and unaffected by the dominance of higher centres. In the human being this simple spinal reflex has been modified tremendously by association with sensations (of touch, smell, sound, sight, etc.) and has become subject to change, either inhibitory or stimulatory, by the highest cortical centres. Even a mere recollection of a smell, a sight or an incident can sometimes excite or inhibit the spinal reflexes. This highlights the importance of accord between the brain and the spine in our sex lives.

The Involuntary Nervous System

The involuntary (or autonomic) nervous system is so called because it controls the activities of various organs of the body, the blood vessels, and various glands and their secretions, without usually impinging on the consciousness. Most of these activities are carried out by a sort of harmony between its two components, namely the sympathetic and the parasympathetic, explained below. Though called involuntary, its activity is closely linked with the somatic nervous system, and integration between the two is effected at various levels. Volitional control of this system is also possible to a certain degree. The activities of the sympathetic and parasympathetic are mutually antagonistic but normally well co-ordinated. When man is healthy their activities dovetail and co-operate to create the best

21

possible environment for the proper functioning of the various body viscera (heart, lungs, liver, etc.) and glands.

The functioning of the involuntary system is important in the context of this book because it is the parasympathetic component which is responsible for the erection of the penis and the clitoris. The centre for it lies in the lower part of the spinal cord. (The nerves leading from this centre are called the *nervi eregentes*.) The sympathetic, on the other hand, is responsible for the contraction of the seminal vesicles, and thereby for ejaculation of the semen. At the same time it causes a constriction of the sphincter of the bladder so that the semen does not flow back into the bladder. Though called sympathetic it is anything but that to a man when its disordered action leads to premature ejaculation.

The huge growth of man's psychic and emotional potential and its effects on the working of the human body are self-evident when one considers that most, if not all, sexual problems are the result of emotional and psychological conflicts. The tranquillity which automatically follows the practice of Yoga tends to resolve these conflicts and, at the same time, harmoniously integrates the working of the nervous system at the brain and spinal cord levels. Once harmony has been achieved between the various components of the nervous system, volitional control not only becomes possible but can be more effectively cultivated through the practice of Yoga.

Importance of Sexual Expression

Yoga can recondition, tone up and develop the sexual prowess of the individual to a greater degree than any tonic or stimulant, and can do it on a sounder and more lasting basis.

There is no direction in existence which says that Hatha Yoga should be exclusively directed towards spirituality, and that it should not be utilized for making your life healthier and happier in every way. Nor is there any doubt that the amount of bitterness and unhappiness existing in people as a result of sexual maladjustment and failure far exceeds that arising from hunger and want. The distress arising from the latter can be overcome with material help. The misery and anguish experienced by people because of sexual frustration are not so easily handled, and often baffle both the physician and the psychiatrist. The mind, the most important of sex organs, registers its ulcers far more deeply than the stomach and duodenum. The scars of the psyche fade much more slowly than those of physical origin.

A sexually weak person is often jealous by nature, and jealousy can contaminate the entire fabric of his life. He can become a victim of persecutory hallucinations or of monomanias, suspicious of conspiracies against him between his wife and friends, or in the case of a woman, between her husband and his female acquaintances. This can result in other unpleasant physical and mental symptoms. Tranquillizers worsen the basic condition by lowering the threshold of mental and physical tolerance, apart from causing unpleasant side-effects. Here, Yoga can step in as a super-tranquillizer, replacing the harmful side-effects with exhilarating benefits.

Yoga's contribution to the brain, or to be more accurate, the mind, is greater than that of drugs. It is sound, real and enduring. The Yoga-tempered urge deepens finer feelings of consideration and love. There is conscious pleasure in giving, and in the realm of sex you will experience gratification in proportion to the pleasure that you learn to give.

Masturbation can relieve tensions arising from apparently non-sexual causes, but Yoga can almost always play this role just as well. It can safely be said that Yoga will, in the first place, divert the mind from masturbation, and that masturbation, when wanted and carried out, will be more pleasant as the orgasm will be comparatively more ecstatic in a body made healthy by Yoga where the tissues are bound to be more alive and responsive. Again, it must be conceded that an orgasm does clear both mind and body. St Paul's oft-quoted words are significant, 'But if they have not continency let them marry, for it is better to marry than to burn.' There is a Chinese proverb which is even more emphatic. 'It is better to satisfy the body than to defile the soul.'

The benefits of sexual intercourse are manifold— tranquillity, forgiveness, tolerance, love, consideration are but a few. An unsatisfied sex urge can lead to frustration, vindictiveness, nervousness, perversions, misanthropy, mental disorders and physical diseases. Efforts to completely suppress sex are never truly successful. However, unbridled licence is not to be recommended either. This and inflexible self-suppression are equally devastating for the average set of nerves.

No man should think of sexual intercourse as the supreme test of his manliness, nor the woman of her femininity. This can destroy the naturalness of a perfectly normal situation and may turn the sex act into a failure. Look upon it as a wonderful and integral part of a healthy and complete life, and never as a competition or a test. While Yoga tones up sex, it is giving you control over it. This control grows and is akin to an efficient switch which you can turn on or off at will instead of letting your energy dissipate wastefully. This control over sex energy is an exclusive gift of Yoga. No other technique known to the physician or the psychiatrist offers this mastery to the individual.

Sometimes boredom and repetition in sex impel the invention of new stimuli which can lead to perversions. There is no doubt that changing postures during the sex act can considerably reduce such tendencies, as the different postures themselves can abundantly satisfy the urge for novelty. The present-day withdrawal of the development of deep love as a precedent to the sex act has proved a major tragedy. It is like a drug which has become a habit without any positive thrill left in it. We now find more sex and less joy. It would be far more desirable to have more intensive joy and less frequent sex. Yoga promotes, to a greater or lesser degree, this wholesome change.

The Kamasanas (different sexual postures) are analogous to the Yogasanas. Some physicians advise middle-aged couples to avoid attempting different sexual positions as they may lead to spraining of muscles, but this problem would not arise in the case of people already accustomed to Yogic positions.

Yoga stabilizes the mind. The practitioner of Yoga will not tremble with fear when approaching sex. A path illuminated by the light of Yoga will remain pure and bright, even when it leads to the fulfilment of Kama. To condemn knowledge of sex as a sin, and to glorify ignorance as bliss, merely promotes unnecessary misery, incompetence, fear and damage to the psyche. People inculcating this psychology may have good intentions, but their results are evil.

25

There is the case of a very orthodox Hindu lady who, while offering herself to a person other than her husband under the irresistibility of her love for him, was so conscious of her sin that she began to recite holy incantations to have her sin forgiven even as the abandon and intensity of passion passed beyond her control. Contrasting sharply with this helplessness before a powerful passion is the example of the wife of Emperor Henry II of Germany, who was canonized as Saint Kunigunde in honour of having remained a virgin until her death. My advice to you is not to marry at all if you are a candidate for such a saintly honour, out of consideration and compassion for your spouse who, if normal and healthy, will have to face a living hell from the mental and physical torture imposed by your pursuit of saintliness.

The right to be mutually happy and contented is fundamental in sex. But it does not stop there. If the result of dissatisfaction in sex tends to turn you into an anti-social being, and if when you are unhappy and discontented you make the lives of those around you miserable and unbearable, then your need for happiness and contentment transcends the fundamental right—it becomes your duty to force yourself to be happy and contented. That goes for the boastful and grumbling celibate as much as for the person who considers unflagging fidelity a passport for inflicting any amount of mental torture on his or her spouse.

The magnitude and splendour of the bliss and ecstasy of a clean, uninhibited and fully abandon-packed sexual union could never contribute to anything derogatory to human dignity. Many a spouse finds himself tied to a partner who insists on conducting sexual acts in the dark. This is like putting in ear plugs before listening to music. Some modern sex specialists even recommend using mirrors to heighten the ecstasy of love-making if the partners adopt a position in which they cannot directly look at each other. There are spouses who consider kissing and caressing as nonsensical, who will not expose their nakedness, and who will surrender their body with reluctance and without offering any co-operation. These people are responsible for an immense loss of happiness both for themselves and their partners. Learning to understand their bodies through Yoga could help them (and their partners) immeasurably. Sexual love should be offered in a spirit of total, loving abandon. This can turn the home into a fount of abiding happiness.

Religion has been seen by some as a safety valve, keeping the mind away from sex. But religion cannot weaken the sex urge, or certainly the austerity has to be very severe and intense to be effective. Unrelieved tensions can lead to physical disorders and can upset glandular balances and metabolic equilibrium. There is no doubt that involvement in other interests such as sport, work, entertainment, etc., does keep the mind away from thoughts of sex during the period of actual involvement, but these pursuits cannot be carried out indefinitely. The best solution therefore lies in using sex itself as the best safety-valve against invasion of the mind by depression, irritation and frustration.

It is said that if some of our political and military leaders had had digestive systems which worked as they should many wars might not have been begun, and countless millions of lives might not have been lost. This could apply with even greater force to sexual satisfaction. A sexually dissatisfied person is angry with the world (including himself) and is therefore unlikely to be safe as a peace-maker. A tranquil and satisfied individual will prove a fairer, more reliable and more effective negotiator. Yoga

27

will, here again, train the individual to be tolerant, accommodating and considerate.

False Notions of Post-coital Exhaustion

We have talked about the benefits of complete and satisfactory love-making, but this will appear questionable to those who have been conditioned to believe that the sexual act is invariably followed by weakness and depression, and who do actually experience exhaustion and unpleasantness after the completion of the sex act. Specialists attribute these feelings to unhealthy indoctrination on the subject of sex. Dr Briffault described the situation admirably when he remarked, 'Post-coital sadness is not a phenomenon of natural history, but of Christian pathology.' Of course this feeling of 'post-coital sadness' is not confined to Christians. You will find this belief prevailing, with similar consequences, among Hindus, Muslims, Jews and many other communities.

In most cases where this depression is experienced the individual is, or has been, heavily under the influence of anti-sex admonitions of religious and social leaders who are frequently totally ignorant of what they are talking about. Coming from an orthodox and conservative community myself, I am reluctant to question the moral integrity or good intentions of these leaders. However, goodness and integrity cannot take precedence over knowledge and familiarity with the subject.

Most of the weakening reactions, such as trembling of the legs, palpitations and so on, arise purely from auto-suggestion. When a person is torn between a violent and irresistible sex urge on one side, and, on the other, extremely disturbing re-

28

ligious injunctions against deriving satisfaction and pleasure from sexual intercourse even with one's own spouse, the sexual life of this person cannot but be filled with complexes. St Jerome's words, 'He who loves his wife too ardently is an adulterer' are guaranteed to implant deep fear among the religious-minded, and this can result in much distress, or indeed a veritable hell.

For many people who have, however, completely severed the spiritual from the physical in the realm of sex, it has become a jaded thing. They are offered and are offering a superfluous pleasure without happiness, instead of yielding the ecstasy which is man's right to expect and enjoy. In the world of sex and love the spirit must regain its place by the side of the body if humanity is to escape the joyless joy of our era, and if the true meaning of sex is to be regained. There is more to beauty than outward appearance. The psyche is a far more developed entity, enveloping an infinite quantum of happiness. Yoga can play a very important role in bringing about this correction.

The universality of the natural sex urge has been brought out by Plato in his *Symposium* in which he describes Aristophanes' theory that man and women are two halves of an original one-piece model, cut in two by the Greek god Zeus. Since then the two separated halves have been impelled to revert to the original through the agency of sexual intercourse. The following passage is highly relevant to the present context as it represents the belief of the uninhibited ancient Greeks in the happy relief experienced by both mind and body after sexual intercourse:

His (Zeus') object in making the change was twofold; if male coupled with female, children might be begotten and the race thus continued,

29

but if male coupled with male, at any rate the desire for intercourse would be satisfied, and men set free from it to turn to other activities and to attend to the rest of the business of life. (Hamilton's translation)

When you compare this statement with Dr Briffault's remark on 'post-coital sadness', you will find that even an unnatural intercourse could afford a sense of satisfaction and release from cares to the ancient Greek whose mind was free from Briffault's 'pathology'.

It is the induced psychological reaction of the participant in the sex act, and not the natural physical or psychic reaction following it, that depresses or exhausts a person. The sufferer may have been led to believe that the love of God, or perhaps of a country, necessitates a hatred for sex. It is for these reasons that the very same sexual acts which gave the Greeks energy and inspiration can today depress the devout followers of religions which denigrate sex and range themselves against the natural expression of a powerful physical and psychic demand and need.

Sex should be recognized as an irrepressible natural urge and treated as an art and a science which can lend colour, beauty, refinement and clean enjoyment to man's existence.

Yoga and Sex Disorders

There are no impotent donkeys, bulls, buffaloes, cats, dogs, wolves, fish, frogs, snakes or lizards, nor are there frigid female creatures among the non-human species. For they have a great advantage over humanity in that their brains leave their spinal cords alone to handle their sex activities.

Sexual performance is one field in which money, position, fame, authority, success, or physical strength or beauty, jointly and severally, are unable to play a decisive role. These factors may help to find a person of your choice, but they cannot ensure a perfect sex act. Even 'true love' may prove utterly ineffective. Confidence, mental health and wholesomeness remain the greatest assets in successfully consummating the sex act. A world champion or beauty queen may be a flop in bed while a seemingly unattractive and insignificant person may have and give a wonderfully satisfactory sexual performance.

Nature has endowed women with a very convenient apparatus to practise deception regarding her interest in sexual intercourse. In this matter men have been sadly let down by nature. If a man hates a woman, in most cases he will not be able to have an erection, the essential prerequisite to full intercourse. A greater tragedy for a man is when he is genuinely attracted to a woman but is unable to get an erection because of fear and anxiety.

The main disorders which plague men—lack of erection, premature ejaculation, absence of seminal discharge at the time of orgasm or the absence of the orgasm itself—are, in most cases, psychological in origin, as are frigidity and fear of coitus in women. A visit to a good psychiatrist is usually helpful, but the regular practice of Yoga goes a long way in toning up not only the neuro-muscular structure of the organs concerned but in steadying and rehabilitating the mind as well.

Sex and Heart Disease

Those suffering from heart disease are advised to follow their doctors' advice on the frequency and method of sexual intercourse. Generally, coitus should take place after a period of physical and mental rest. The active role should mainly be taken over by the healthier partner in a position particularly comfortable to the heart patient. The act should be performed in the nude or, at very least, no tight-fitting garments should be worn. Relaxing Yogasanas such as Vajrasana and Shavasana, with regulated Pranayama, will help to keep away further recurrence of the disease. The Ayurvedic dictum, 'Stop your exercise (including sexual) before you become breathless', should be meticulously followed.

I must add that even then those suffering from heart disease should indulge in the minimum sexual intercourse necessary to combat the ill effects of suppression.

Yoga, Aphrodisiacs and Placebos

The demands of sex on the physical faculties, when they become excessive in frequency and intensity, necessitates replenishment of energy. The measures which lead to the restoration and toning up of sexual efficiency and improvement of sexual performance go under the name of alteratives. Those which arouse and intensify the sex urge are called aphrodisiacs.

Both the ancients and the moderns rightly believe that there is no aphrodisiac greater than the sexual partner who is the personification of the physical and mental qualities to which you react with warmth, love, desire and passion.

The following passage from Charaka Samhita typically represents the psychology of all men, but this text can suitably be reversed and applied to the psychology of women.

The best means of stimulating one's desire and virility (the best aphrodisiac or the best agent of virilification) is an exhilarating sexual partner in the woman. When the desired sense-objects yield great pleasure even if singly experienced by the senses (soft touch, beautiful sight, entrancing musical sounds, sweet fragrance and delicious taste), then what need be said of the person of the woman in whom the delectable objects of all the senses are found established together. Such a combination of the delectable objects of all the senses is found only in the person of the woman and nowhere else. . . . Hence it is that man's pleasure is mainly in the woman. . . . In her also are established righteousness, wealth, auspiciousness and the two worlds—this and the other. . . .

She, who is the best of women for a man and endears herself to him quickly by virtue of her age, form, speech and gestures either as a result of destiny or of the merits of acts (*i.e.* good deeds) in this very life, who is the delight of his heart, who returns his love in equal measure, who is akin to him in mind, who is amenable to and is pleased with his advances, who enthralls his senses by her excellent qualities, separated from whom he feels the world to be desolate and joyless, but for whom he feels his body a burden and as if devoid of its senses, at the sight of whom he is untouched by grief, distress, depression or fear, approaching whom he gains confidence, seeing whom he gets greatly elated, whom he approaches daily as if for the first time, and united with whom in sex repeatedly, he remains yet unsatisfied; such a woman is the best of virilific to him. (Jamnagar translation)

The quaintness of style is due to the fact that the original was written thousands of years ago.

The following passage from Charaka is very significant in that it not only justifies the adoption of such measures as the use of aphrodisiacs for maintenance of virility, but sees them as a man's essential duty towards himself and his partner.

The man of self-restraint should seek, always, to maintain his virility by adoption of virilifying measures, for righteousness, wealth, affection and good repute are dependent on the maintenance of healthy manhood.

Yoga helps you achieve these objectives without your having to resort to any of these measures. If sex is cultivated as a cultural activity and art, and not merely and ignorantly kept pinned down to the genitals, it simply refuses to grow old, and can give the same thrill in the nineties as it gave during the teens or the twenties, and, quite probably, more so.

Musk, ginseng, opium, strychnine, cantharides, alcohol, hashish, yohimbin, *Cannabis indica* and a number of other Ayurvedic and Unani herbs and drugs, and of course erotic dances, nudes and sexual photographs have been used to stimulate the sex urge and to prolong the duration of the sex act. Some of them do help some people to a greater or lesser extent either by actually acting as stimulants or tranquillizers, or merely acting as placebos.

Eminent specialists in the field of sex have recorded again and again the placebo character of the so-called sex tonics and aphrodisiacs. Perhaps no other human function is influenced so deeply by thought processes as sexual activity. Since the individual background and experience of repression and inhibition differ in every individual, the effects of repression also differ. This explains the great variety of symptoms met with among them—peptic ulcers, chronic catarrh, mucous colitis, palpitations, anxiety neuroses, melancholias, nightmares, constipation, hysteria, and of course impotence and frigidity.

Dr Edward S. Gifford Jr records a revealing case of the treatment of a sexual disorder, psychological in origin, with the use of a placebo. (*The Charms of Love*, Doubleday 1962.) The Doctor had given a 55-year-old technician at the Johns Hopkins Hospital in Baltimore an injection of the synthetic male hormone, testosterone. The technician experienced a very satisfying improvement in his sexual tone. 'A month later,' says the report, 'he (the technician) felt that another injection was needed to maintain his sexual vigour. This time, however, doctors injected sterile oil that contained no drug. It was take from a bottle which they had labelled ''Testosterone'' and which they had carefully placed where the man could read the label. The technician happily reported that the results from the second injection were just as good as the first. Each time thereafter that he returned for the injection he was given one of oil. But his resultant sexual vigour continued to enliven his evenings, and sexual excitement began to interfere with his work during the day.'

Yoga tends to prevent and ameliorate these conditions of repression and their resulting effects. Yoga is not only a substitute for youth, it is an improvement on it. It transcends youth where inflexibility of inexperience and inconsiderateness of undeveloped spirituality can sometimes mar the richness of mutuality. A Yoga-trimmed body has also a Yoga-trimmed mind.

The role of behaviour in sex is highly important. An utterly dissatisfied women may smile sweetly and thank you for the 'thrill' you gave her—and a fully satisfied woman may, out of stubbornness, or false notions of prudery, with one ugly gesture of pseudo-frustration, tell you that you have failed to

35

give her any pleasure. You will covet the former, and the chances are your performance with her will improve with every successive meeting with her, while you may never be able to meet the latter in a sexually successful act.

If people find the use of 'four letter words' sexually stimulating there can be no possible moral objection to it, although these are not, in my opinion, a proven aphrodisiac. Nor is there any harm in changes of places and postures in sex if they contribute to the happiness of the couple.

In the famous classic *Sahitya Darpana* there is a passage stating that the grace of shyness in a heroine is an ornamental asset, but this very asset turns into an ugly defect if exhibited by her in bed at the time of giving herself to her lover. It is a sound truth and the ancients did well to convey it to the youth at the time of their education.

A woman takes about four times as long as a man to become fully stimulated to enjoy sex. Yoga controls haste in a man and gives him time to wait with patience to let the urge of the female join up with his own for the greater benefit and pleasure of both. Many women still believe that it is the man's job to initiate them in sex and set the pace. At any rate, many want the men to do so. They are wrong. Women can arouse men powerfully if they initiate the preliminaries.

It is not that every woman is slow in reaching the height of her sexual desires. A Sanskrit poet puts the following words into the mouth of his heroine, who addressing one of her female friends says, 'You are lucky enough to describe the joys of sex which you experience with your lover. I do not know them. For with the first touch of my lover, I lose myself in an ecstasy and at that stage all thinking and remembering comes to a standstill.' The implication as to who is 'lucky' is clear!

Yoga and Intoxicants

Alcohol, opium, cannabis, and other similar drugs on which their users lean for their ability to perform the sex act do not, in reality, tone up any part of the nervous system, or the sexual apparatus. They merely neutralize the inhibitions by doping the individual. In the case of a large number of those addicted to alcohol or drugs, sex loses its importance altogether. The euphoria or hallucination induced by these drugs becomes itself the sole objective. They may eliminate not only any interest in sex, but may destroy the very capacity to consummate the sex act.

The spinal cord with its sex centre is left alone by the intoxicants, but since they dull the brain and interfere with the influence of the brain on the spinal centres, the user is freed from the undesirable complexes which plague the human race. After these drugs take full effect, man and animal share an identity as man is then no longer subject to inhibitions. The sex act becomes, as in animals, a purely spinal sex act, bypassing the heaven, or the hell, which the brain can make of it.

Tranquillizers and stimulants and even gonadotropic hormones have not proved of much help in relieving distress arising from sexual disorders. How much better it is to administer Yoga, and to take away alcohol, yohimbin, hashish, and even the hormones which frequently prove ineffective. Why not actually and basically strengthen the entire sex apparatus from the brain down to the external genitals through Yogic practices, rather than indulging in repeated chemical stimulation? The latter is bound to blunt the very keenness, the edge, of the instinct. The individual progressively becomes an alcoholic or drug addict and, while he may endeavour to hold on to the practice of sex, this will gradually lose its meaning, its real thrill and sparkle, its explosive ecstasy and undiluted fulfilment, because of the very drugs resorted to in order to enhance these effects. The widespread use of intoxicants is an explicit index of the importance people attach to an effective performance of the sex act. Yoga beats all these measures in the attainment of sexual objectives as it tones up the sex centres on a sounder and more lasting basis, prolonging youth and promoting longevity. It imparts alertness to the mind instead of making it full. The smile on the face of an alcoholic is owlish and leery. The smile on the face of a Yogi is radiant.

Drugs enslave the addict. Yoga imparts mastery, both mental and physical. In contrast to drug-taking, a sudden break in the practice of Yoga makes no difference—it will take years to undo the benefits of Yoga unless one actively dissipates oneself. Yoga integrates, drugs disintegrate the psyche. The benefits of one are real and abiding, of the other, illusory and fleeting.

Yoga builds up a philosophical outlook on life, conducive to psychological maturity. The energy it gives imparts less heat and more light. The passage of years does not lead to irritability, frustration, or the helplessness of impotent and decrepit old age, but to pleasant, serene, mellow and mature wisdom. Even in advanced years, health seems to radiate from all parts of the body, sex not excepted.

Emotions such as anger, hate, jealousy, greed, etc. affect both the muscular and nervous systems adversely. Yoga gradually leads to control and conquest of these emotions, not to suppression. The difference between control and suppression is analogous to steadiness and obstinacy, forgiveness and helplessness. A muscular system trained to bend and not break will nullify the injurious effects of anger and allied emotions.

The paleness of the skin and complexion in fear or anger, the dryness of the mouth, the clamminess of the skin, the rapid beating of the heart, dilation of the pupils, the twitching of muscles can all happen to a nervous person approaching the sexual act. What sort of success can such a tense individual make of sex? Even with the best of intentions, the effort will be a failure. The answer is the development of intelligent relaxation through Yoga, not relaxation through drugs which befuddle the mind.

Yoga can be compared to an amphibious tank which is neither so fast on land as the best of cars, nor so fast on water as the best of speedboats, but can negotiate both. The excellence of Yoga lies in the fact that acting simultaneously on mind and body it overcomes most of the impediments of both areas. Yoga excels the best of physical exercises in its action on the body tissues, and the best of sedatives, tranquillizers or 'brain tonics', if any such exist, in its action on the mind.

Sex and Intellectual Maturity

Man, standing at the top of creation, has many advantages over other creatures, but whereas the animal has only to reach the natural limits of its physical growth, man has constantly to develop in order to attain proper maturity. Man is quite capable of both raising himself far above the beast, or becoming much worse than any beast.

Anger, wrath and jealousy are signs of immaturity and weakness. The frequency of anger in a child is greater than in most adults. This child/adult analogy can be extended to the weak and the strong, the ill and the healthy, the mentally disturbed and the mentally strong. A physically strong man may be mentally or culturally weak. There are people who are even (or especially) jealous of the success and popularity of their own spouse, when they should be happy and proud for them. These people need education, not condemnation. Yoga demonstrates that man can and should continue to improve upon himself, physically, morally and spiritually. Finally, according to the claims of the Yogis, he can even transcend himself, though this may be far from your immediate aims.

The first aphorism in *Yoga Darshan*, the most authentic classic in Yoga, deals with the development of mastery of the mind. You order your mind to perform for you, and not vice-versa. You control the mind so that you can permit it to build up a strong passion, and you can also divert it and order it to keep clear of all desires. It will increase your capacity to bear stress, and contribute to your spiritual and intellectual maturity.

An animal eats when it is hungry, drinks when it is thirsty, indulges in sex when it is passionate. Man can create hunger when he is not normally hungry, can create thirst, and can create sexual desire if he is not suffering from any inhibitions. He can step outside nature; the animal cannot. He can even step outside himself, to look at himself objectively. It is at this stage that he is truly a mature man. Yoga's contribution to this development is greater than any other single factor.

A number of authors have advocated the gathering of experience through having sexual intercourse with a number of people before marriage. They prescribe this remedy in the interests of permanency and stability of marriage. You will hold me guilty of evasion of my duty towards you if I do not comment on this question. The comment is very simple.

The entire question revolves around the *maturity* of the individual. Much of the unhappiness in sexual life flows from arrest in the development of maturity. Pettiness, selfishness, jealousy, possessiveness are all attributes of an immature mind. Tolerance, forgiveness and consideration represent a state of higher development. If these desirable traits have had a proper chance to be cultivated by an individual, it would be of little consequence whether a person has had sexual experience or not.

Yoga, Ego, Attitudes and Relationships

Man has a peculiar attitude towards sex. The laws he applies to other instincts are not applied to it, as a rule. A man will offer his food to another, even when he is hungry and the other is not. But he will not usually offer his beloved to any person, even one who is dying of sexual desire while he himself is utterly satiated or impotent. This attitude is reflected by woman too with regard to her lover.

There is an analogy between appetite and love on one hand, and hunger and sexual desire on the other. In the case of real hunger or lust there is little choosiness displayed; but the quality of the food and the partner assume great importance in the case of a moderate appetite and love respectively.

'For the large-hearted, the entire world constitutes his or her family' says an old Sanskrit text. If you treat the entire world as your kith and kin, how very close will you be to your partner. True lovers will feel a closeness despite a physical separation of thousands of miles. In contrast, many modern couples lying together in bed, even while making love perhaps, may be miles from each other and busy calculating the terms and the costs of an intended divorce.

41

It is mainly due to this quality of experiencing proximity despite distances that men of understanding and sympathy, devoted to their causes and ideals, can keep their emotional and intellectual contacts alive and intact, sometimes despite years of solitary confinement. They refuse to crack or let their spirits break under any stress or strain. Conversely, men whose sole contacts rest with their own egos and who cannot get over their emotional aloofness even in the midst of their 'loved' ones, disintegrate due to their self-imposed isolation based on immaturity and all-consuming (and mostly baseless) grudges and jealousies.

Yoga is a psychosomatic language which replaces marriage guidance counsellors and psychiatrists. It can turn antagonists into co-operators. There is communication and adjustment in Yoga-induced and Yoga-controlled relationships.

It is naturally more considerate and decent to give your partner a feeling that your love for him or her constitutes a total emotional and spiritual response to his or her personality as a whole. Your partner must never be allowed to feel that your entire interest is confined to the genitals, and begins and ends with the sexual act. The spiritual must be co-ordinated with the sexual in a truly satisfactory relationship.

Be very careful not to hurt the ego of your partner by thinking and talking only about yourself, for nothing destroys the zest and free abandonment of sex as the wounded ego of a person. Cultivation of consideration can keep mutual attraction and emotional proximity at their peak until the end of life. The practice of Yoga helps you attain these desirable objectives. When a practitioner of Yoga says 'I love you' it is a much more intense statement than the much abused utterance which is bandied about in social circles. In fact, for the practitioner of Yoga, it is hardly necessary actually to utter these words. The unspoken, silent and spontaneous expression of the Yoga-streamlined partner radiates this most positive of emotions deeply and effectively.

The Asanas

43

The Asanas

General Instructions 🐉
1 Wake up before sunrise. This practice tones up
the muscles of the eye as it protects the pupil of the
eye against its sudden contraction which will
inevitably result if the eye is opened in full daylight.
Yoga always advises avoidance of sudden move-
ments or jerks in all bodily activities. By rising

before sunrise, you allow the pupil to take in the light gradually. As the sun rises, the pupil contracts slowly and gradually without its neuro-muscular structure contracting suddenly with a jerk.

If, however, the nature of your work or routine forces upon you the need to sleep late, see that you wake up in a room where sunlight, or even daylight, does not fall directly on your eyes when you wake up, and where you can slowly and gradually get accustomed to light before they are subjected to the full impact of daylight.

Another benefit of rising early is that you get a surplus of time in the morning which can protect you against jitters and nervousness arising out of rushing your morning activities to catch up with your office time. With a little more time at your disposal, you can go about your morning duties with a relaxed mind, a prerequisite to the practice of Yoga, and can easily extract your half-an-hour for the regular practice of Yoga. Thus, beginning your day with a cool and relaxed mind, instead of in a huff and a hurry, this tranquil beginning of the day may reflect beneficially on all your activities throughout the day. This little change in routine in getting up earlier may make all the difference to your career and your relationships with others.

2 Ensure cleanliness of the bowels. If your diet is correct, and you observe punctuality and regularity with regard to the time of moving your bowels, you are not likely to suffer from constipation. Once the regular habits are formed, and the Yogic exercises are commenced, your chances of remaining free from constipation are considerably improved.

3 Your bowels must be clean at the time of practising the Asanas and Pranayama (Yogic exercises and breathing). Yoga is best practised on a clean bowel and an empty stomach. You are permitted   45

Fig. 1 Correct

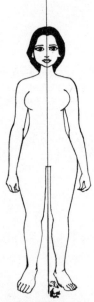

Fig. 2 Correct

to take a hot or cold bath before performing your exercises, if it suits your routine, but you can perform them even without taking a bath. You can have a hot bath any time after the exercise but you cannot take a cold bath within fifteen minutes of completion of the Yogic exercises. Again, it is very desirable to have a bath daily but it is not absolutely essential in exceptionally cold climates. It may, however, be mentioned that both the hot and the cold baths are aphrodisiacs and are desirable from many angles—hygienic, tonic, aesthetic and, of course, aphrodisiac. You will start enjoying cold baths even in cold climates once you start your Yoga earnestly and regularly.

4 You can go through your exercises either in the morning or in the afternoon when the stomach is empty and the bowels clean. The duration of exercises should range from 15 to 45 minutes according to your capacity and the stage you have reached in the practice of your Asanas. Breakfast can be taken 30 minutes after completing the exercises but this period can be reduced to as little as 5 minutes, if you happen to be a very busy person. Remember that an empty bowel is a necessity before the exercises and not after them. If you want to give a demonstration of the Asanas before your friends, better choose an evening rather than a morning as the body is generally more flexible during the latter part of the day. If you perform your exercises in the evening, you are not to eat anything for at least 3 hours preceding the commencement of the exercises. This is to accommodate the needs of modern life. The classical Yogic demand is a 4-hour abstinence from food preceding the exercises.

5 If you practise prayer or meditation, it should usually be performed sitting in Sukhasana (Easy

Pose—See Plate 1A) or Padmasana (Lotus Pose—Plate 1B), before or after you do your pranayamic breathing exercises. If your prayers involve any rituals or visits to any shrines, better finish the Yogic exercises and breathing before commencing your religious practices. This will improve your concentration for prayer and meditation.

6 Both when practising Yoga and when not practising it, develop a habit of checking and rechecking your posture while standing or sitting and go on correcting the faulty posture, again and again, and day after day, until it becomes an unconscious habit with you. Sit and stand erect without sagging or hunching and without becoming stiff in your attempt at being erect. A large number of people associate erect posture with stiffness. This is unfortunate. The true posture is, both while standing or sitting, a *straight but relaxed* posture which you can easily develop through sustained practice of Yoga. (Figs 1, 2, 3, 4.)

Fig. 3 Correct

7 Begin with the practice of easier Asanas first. As the body acquires greater flexibility, add, gradually, to your practice comparatively more difficult Asanas. In trying to practise Asanas which are not easy for you to perform, stop at the stage when the pain becomes unpleasant. 'Pleasant pain' is the boundary line up to which you can stretch your effort without restraining yourself. Remember that **the most difficult pose is not necessarily the most beneficial pose. Should pain continue, consult a doctor immediately.**

8 Relax your body with the following preliminary bending exercises before doing the Yogic ones:

    (a) Stand erect with both your feet joined together, heel with heel and big toe with big toe.

Fig. 4 Incorrect

47

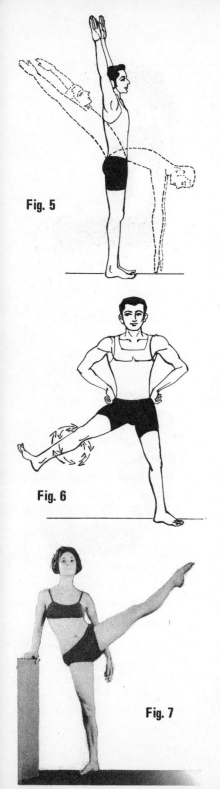

Fig. 5

Fig. 6

Fig. 7

There should be no distance between the two big toes as is found in the stance adopted in modern exercises.

(b) Raise your arms as high as you can and bend your body backwards. Keep the legs steady and let the trunk go back as far as it can. Having reached the limit of your capacity to bend backward, start moving forward until your fingers touch the ground or the toes of your feet. Practise these bends ten times (Fig. 5). Breathe in when raising your hands from the ground and taking your body backward. Breathe out while bending forward. If you cannot cover one full backward movement in one inhalation and one full forward movement in one exhalation, stop in the process of bending, inhale or exhale your breath as needed, and resume the movement and the breathing where you left off.

(c) With your arms held against your waist on both sides, raise one leg as high up as you can and rotate it ten times, first clock-wise and then anti-clock-wise. Bring the leg back into position and repeat the exercise with the other leg. In both cases make your foot describe as large a circle during the rotation as possible (Fig. 6). A photograph of Miss Lally (Fig. 7) has been included to show how high a leg can be raised for rotation if the body is well trained.

(d) Keeping your hands slightly away from your body, and standing erect with your feet slightly apart, rotate your pelvis, first clock-wise and then anti-clock-wise, ten times in each case (Fig. 8). You can place your hands on your waist as in (c) above to make it easier for you during the first few days or weeks of commencing the exercise.

(e) Similarly, holding the arms slightly away from your body with elbows partly relaxed, rotate your trunk first clock-wise and then anti-clock-wise, ten times in each case (Fig. 9). Here, too, you can place your hands on your waist as in (c) above to make the exercise easier.

(f) If short of time, reduce bends and rotations from ten each to five each, *or even one each.*

Asanas (Yogic Postures)

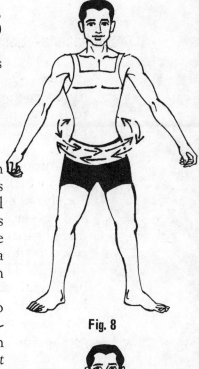

Fig. 8

Some of my readers have reported improvement in their sexual performance after practising the Asanas (postures) prescribed primarily for relief of spinal pain. This was to be expected, as the sex centre is situated in the lower spine, and a healthy spine will contribute, to a greater or a lesser degree, to a healthy sex centre. This will involve some repetition of the old Asanas.

I believe you will be happier if this book comes to you as a complete unit by itself. In order to compensate those of you who are already familiar with the Asanas from my earlier book, *Yoga Against Spinal Pain*, I have introduced a much larger number of Asanas in this book giving the reader considerably more extensive material in photographs and postures than before.

Some of the Asanas, which the ancient Yogic texts have originally recommended for sublimation of the sex urge to promote celibacy among those involved in spiritual pursuits, will also prove to be excellent exercises for toning up the sex centres.

The Asanas described on the following pages, while contributing in varying degrees to general stability, strength, resilience, efficiency, flexibility and effective and satisfying functioning of all organs and tissues of the body, have a particular slant towards a rejuvenating, toning and sustaining effect on the sex centres (including the entire urogenital apparatus) of both men and women.

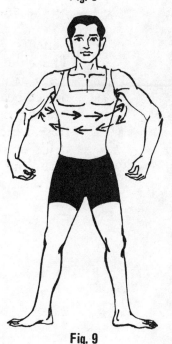

Fig. 9

1A
Sukhasana—Easy Pose

Posture ☙

Sit on the ground. Fold your legs at the knees in such a way that one foot rests inside the knee-fold of the other leg and the other foot is on the ground beneath the knee-fold of the opposite leg, as shown in the plate.

Although the best pose for practising Yoga is Padmasana (Lotus Pose) which is described overleaf, the Sukhasana, being much easier, is widely practised by laymen in India at the time of meditation, worship and prayer. In the villages where people gather for a social chat or formal meetings or festive functions, or even in the houses where the only place to sit is on a carpet or a bare floor, Sukhasana is the pose generally adopted. Therefore, those of you who cannot perform Padmasana to begin with can use Sukhasana until you learn to sit comfortably in the Lotus Pose, and all the postures and Yogic breathing exercises which should be performed while sitting in the Lotus Pose can be practised in Sukhasana.

Benefits ☙

The chief advantage of this posture is its availability to beginners in Yoga as a vehicle for Pranayama (Yogic breath culture) which has a direct bearing on reconditioning the nervous system and an indirect bearing on sexual performance. It is also a restful and tranquillizing pose which eliminates exhaustion and fatigue after strenuous games, drills or heavy manual labour. For relaxing the muscles of the body, including those related to the spine, Sukhasana is only bettered by Shavasana (Pose of Tranquillity) and Vajrasana (Hardy Pose).

1B
Padmasana—Lotus Pose

Posture ✦

Sit down on the ground with both your legs loosely stretched in front of you. Taking hold of your right foot by the ankle, place it on your left thigh with the heel so close to the body that it presses against the left groin. Without disturbing the position of the right foot flex your left knee so that the left foot comes near the body. Lift it by the ankle and place it on your right thigh with the heel of the left foot pressing against the right groin. The soles of the two feet in this position will be pointing skywards like the petals of a full-blown lotus flower. Hence the term 'Lotus Pose'. Hold this pose with your dorsal and thoracic spine erect. Place your hands on your knees as shown in the photograph.

The Lotus Pose is an important basic pose in the practice of Yoga around which many other vital Yogic poses have been devised. This is the best pose for practising Pranayama—i.e., the Yogic breathing exercises. Those who are too obese to complete this pose can either sit in Sukhasana (Easy Pose), the preceding posture, or can just put the right foot on the left thigh for three minutes and then change over and place the left foot on the right thigh for three minutes, thus practising only half of the pose at a time. This can be continued until sufficient flexibility is developed to perform the Lotus Pose without difficulty.

Benefits ✦

This posture is a superior version of the Easy Pose (Sukhasana) and bestows all the benefits of Sukhasana in a much greater degree. The Yogis attribute to this posture the capacity to stimulate the functioning of the spinal cord and to improve the Yogic breathing and its effectiveness on the entire respiratory system. The practice of Pranayama while sitting in this posture keeps the spinal column firmly erect and tends to cure the stoop. It tones up the inguinal areas and counters tendency to inguinal hernia. It also contributes to a tranquillity of mind and is therefore recommended as the ideal posture for meditation, concentration and study.

2
Vajrasana—Hardy Pose

Posture 🕉
Kneel on the ground with your knees, ankles and big toes touching it. Then sit down on your heels. If you feel too much pressure from your weight on your feet you can move the heels outwards and then sit on them to distribute the weight over a larger portion of the soles. Place your hands on your knees, sit erect but relaxed. Keep the eyes open and keep the breathing slow and deep. The chest should be expanded and abdomen drawn inwards.

Benefits 🕉
The great advantage of Vajrasana over all other postures is that it can be practised even by very advanced cases of heart disease. Also, unlike

any other Asana except Vistrita Pada Vajrasana (see page 57), it can be practised immediately after meals, however heavy.

Apart from its strengthening effect on the spine which I have dealt with in *Yoga Against Spinal Pain*, it improves the tone of the sexual organs in the male and the female. It is also supposed to be beneficial in cases of neuralgic headaches, sloth, stiffness, anger, anxiety, worry, cowardice, fear, hesitation, weakness and laxity of the sexual organs including the male and female gonads, thinness of semen and weak functioning of the kidneys. It effectively reduces flatulence and improves digestion. It prolongs youth and postpones old age. It contributes to self-confidence. The Yogis consider it a must for patients with heart disease. It is easy to perform and for patients of pronounced and discomforting flatulence it should be practised, in addition to regular morning exercises, after the two principal meals.

IMPORTANT: No other variety of Vajrasana should be performed immediately after meals except this and Vistrita Pada Vajrasana.

3A
Nata Vajrasana—Forward-bend Hardy Pose

Posture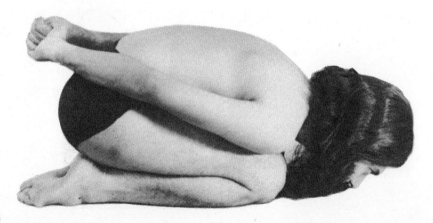
Sit down in Vajrasana (Hardy Pose—see Plate 2) with both hands interlocked behind the back instead of being placed on the knees. Then bend your trunk slowly forward till your abdomen and chest comes into full contact with your thighs, and your chin and nose touch the ground in front of you. Hold this pose for ten seconds or longer. Keep your eyes open. Take deep and slow breaths.

Unlike the simple Vajrasana, Nata Vajrasana should not be performed immediately after meals. It must only be performed, along with other Asanas, on an empty stomach.

Benefits
As long as it is remembered that the Nata Vajrasana is not to be performed on a full stomach, the practice of this Asana confers all the benefits of the Vajrasana in a greater degree. In particular, its contribution to the flexibility of the spine and improvement of the tone of the sexual organs in both the sexes is more marked.

istrita Pada Vajrasana—Hardy Pose with Parted Feet

Posture

Kneel down on the ground, spreading your feet as far apart as you can while keeping the knees together, so that you are sitting on the ground between your feet which are at a considerable distance from your body. Keep both your hands on your respective knees, sit erect but relaxed, keep the eyes open and continue slow and deep breathing.

Benefits

Like other Asanas which are practised by the Yogis for sublimation of the sex urge, this can also benefit the family man by toning up his sex centres.

Like the simple Vajrasana it can be practised after meals. It combines the benefits of the Vajrasana and the Gorakshasana poses (see page 67) as it is derived from both.

4
Supta Vajrasana—Horizontal Hardy Pose

Posture

Kneel on the ground with the knees, ankles and big toes together as in
Vajrasana (Hardy Pose). Then without shifting the position of the toes
and the knees and only just separating the heels to make a place for
your seat, bend slowly backwards till your head, shoulders and back
touch the ground behind you. Keep both your hands on your thighs.
The back should be in contact with the ground as much as possible.
The eyes can be kept open or closed. Continue deep breathing. Remain
as relaxed as possible during the posture.

IMPORTANT Pregnant women should avoid this Pose.

Benefits &

Supta Vajrasana exercises the muscles and the blood vessels of the feet, knees, abdomen, ribs, throat and neck, mouth, eyes and the head and benefits all these parts. The exerciser experiences a stretching sensation along the whole length of the body. In spite of this, most of you will feel that the sensation of relaxation experienced while exhaling in this pose, and particularly at the end of exhalation, is even deeper and more soothing and tranquillizing than that experienced during the Shavasana (Tranquillity Pose) itself. The stretch on the inguinal muscles and blood vessels exercises a toning effect on the sex organs and the pelvic viscera. It also corrects certain defects of the spine, alleviates backache and tones up both the deep and the superficial muscles of the spine as well as its sex centres.

5
Gomukhasana—Cow-head Pose (Front and Back Views)

Posture ✿
Sit on the ground with your right leg bent so that the centre of the rim of your heel is under the anus. The centre of gravity of the body should now be straight on the right heel on which the anus is resting. Now bend the left leg so as to bring the left heel as near the right hip as possible (see Plate 5A). In this posture, the left knee should be just above the right knee so that a straight line joining the two knees will fall perpendicular to the ground. Sitting in this posture, take your right hand behind your back so that your elbow bend is in contact with your head. Then take your left hand behind your back keeping the left elbow under your shoulder. Then lock both your hands together behind your back as shown in Plate 5A. The front aspect of the posture is shown in Plate 5B. Keep the eyes open, body straight and abdomen drawn inwards. Continue slow and deep breathing.

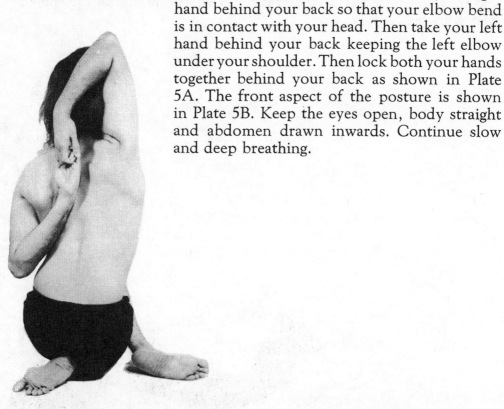

Benefits

This posture improves the circulation in the armpits and the sides. It also tones up the tissues of the feet, the knees and the waist. It improves the circulation and tones up the muscles, tendons and ligaments of the knees and the calves. The practice of this Asana, alternating the position of the arms and the legs so that both sides receive equal and balanced toning, improves the circulatory activity of both the lungs. It has been recommended for those suffering from tuberculosis of the lungs and it is beneficial to patients with asthma. It is very helpful in relieving backache, and can remove feelings of weakness and fatigue and of dislike for food. It also tends to reduce hyperacidity (heartburn).

In particular, it effectively tones up the perineum, the prostate, the male and female genitalia and the rectal muscles. It prevents nocturnal emissions and in a number of cases has proved an effective cure for piles. It also relieves constipation. Its regular practice considerably counters the commonest of sex complaints—premature ejaculation—thereby improving sexual performance.

6
Ardha Matsyendrasana—Incomplete Matsyendra Pose 1
(Front and Back Views)

Posture 🕉

Matsyendra was the name of a great ancient Indian Yogi whose habitual posture was named after him as Matsyendrasana. Here, the name of the posture is preceded by 'Ardha' (Sanskrit for half or incomplete), for the beginner will find it difficult to perform the complete posture.

To perform this incomplete posture, sit on the ground and spread the left leg in front of you at right angles to your trunk. Then place the right foot on the ground on the left side of your left knee as shown in the plate. Then pass your left arm round the right side of the left knee and hold your right foot with your left hand. Take your right hand behind your back, placing the back of your right hand on the extreme left of your waist. Continue deep breathing, expanding your chest as far as possible. Turn the head to your right as far as it can go so that the chin is in line with your shoulder. Keep the eyes open. Do not let the

knee of the left leg rise from the ground. Try to press your abdomen with your right thigh while in this position.

Repeat the same in reverse by stretching the right leg and putting the left foot beside the right knee, and so on.

Benefits

This posture is usually prescribed for people with weak kidneys and lax urinary (bladder) muscles. It alleviates spermatorrhoea in the case of men and leucorrhoea due to mild inflammatory condition in the case of women. It tones up the entire urogenital apparatus, thereby considerably improving the sexual performance in both sexes. Leucorrhic discharge resulting from serious lesions like cancer, abscesses, or venereal infections would, of course, need medical treatment under expert guidance.

7A
Ardha Matsyendrasana—Incomplete Matsyendra Pose 2

Posture 🐾
The same as for Incomplete Matsyendra Pose 1, except that the stretched leg is drawn in so that the heel touches the opposite hip.

Benefits 🐾
The same as from the previous pose.

Purna Matsyendrasana—Complete Matsyendra Pose

Posture

The complete Matsyendrasana is much more difficult than the incomplete poses described on the previous pages and can either be abandoned altogether or left until greater flexibility has been developed through practice of the previous Asanas.

Sit on the ground and place the left foot on the right thigh as you do in the Lotus Pose. The heel of the left foot is near the navel. Now raise your right foot and place it beside the left knee as you did in the incomplete Pose 1, the difference being that here the right leg is not stretched. See that the entire sole of your right foot by the side of the left knee is touching the ground and does not leave it. Then bring your left arm around the right knee and catch hold of the toes of the right foot with your left hand exactly as you did in the Incomplete Matsyendra Pose 2. In the same manner take your right arm behind your back and bring it to a position so that it touches the left heel, instead of just the waist as in the former posture. Turn the head to the right bringing the chin into line with the right shoulder.

Repeat the Asana in reverse placing the right foot on the left thigh and changing the position of the limbs in the preceding posture.

Benefits ✣

This posture compresses the alimentary canal and almost all the viscera lying in the thorax, the abdomen, and the pelvis. It also twists the spine alternately on either side and stretches the muscles of the legs and the arms. When fully accomplished, the Matsyendra posture hardly leaves any portion of the body unexercised and unstimulated.

Yogis prescribe it for disorders of the liver and the spleen particularly when they become chronic. It is very beneficial in chronic backache, toning up the nerves, and the deep as well as the superficial muscles of the spine. It improves the circulation of the entire body, increasing the efficiency of the spine and the spinal sex centre in particular. By maintaining deep breathing during this pose, the exerciser accelerates the blood circulation of all the glands and viscera from thyroid down to pelvis, including the sex glands. It also improves digestion and assimilation of food and alleviates dyspepsia. Some Yogis go as far as to attribute anthelmintic properties to this posture—i.e., destruction of worms found in the alimentary canal. How far it is effective in killing and expelling the worms is not possible to corroborate as no controlled experiments have been done, but there is no doubt that the practice of Matsyendra is very beneficial to the exerciser in search of sound health, sound sex life and longevity. It is a difficult pose and only through long practice and patience can average men and women master it. It is for this particular reason that I have offered a compromise in the form of the incomplete Matsyendrasana to enable the exerciser to gain some, if not all, the benefits of this posture.

Gorakshasanas—Goraksha Poses 1–6

Goraksha Poses are named after one of the greatest and most 'perfected' of Yogis and mystics of ancient India, Goraksha or Gorakhanatha. There is no end to the stories and legends recounting the miracles and supernatural deeds performed by this Yogi of Yogis. It is appropriate that the postures should be associated with the name of one whose control over the sex urge was so complete that while he could perform the sex act at will at the highest level of efficiency, giving and deriving the maximum ecstasy, he could also totally sublimate the urge at will and switch off to complete detachment from sexual matters. Such mastery over the sex urge certainly lies within human potential but I do not expect any one of you to approach Yoga with the dedication and persistent endeavour which is necessary to reach that state of development. Our aims are more modest and will be fully met by the practice of the series of Gorakshasanas that follow, or even the practice of one or two of them.

8A
Goraksha Pose 1 (Bhadrasana—Good Pose)

Posture 🕉

Goraksha Pose 1 is referred to by some Yogis as Bhadrasana (Good Pose), a term which can also be applied to a type of Vajrasana (Hardy Pose). It is enough to remember this pose as Goraksha Pose 1.

Sit on the ground with your right knee pointing to your extreme right and the left knee pointing to your extreme left. In trying to do so, you will have to fold your legs inwards so that the calves are fully in contact with the thighs. Now join the soles of your feet together so that from the heels to the toes they are in full contact. Keeping the knees in touch with the ground, or holding them as close to the ground as you can manage during the earlier stages of practice, draw in your joined feet close to your body so that the heels of both the feet are touching the inner extremity of your thighs, or, better still, your perineum if you can draw the heels further inwards (Plate 8A). Hold the pose, with both your hands on your knees and your trunk as erect as possible, for a minimum of ten seconds. Keep your eyes open and continue deep breathing.

Benefits 🕉

This posture tones up the nerves, the muscles and the circulatory system of the perineum and the genital organs of both men and women. Yogis believe that it improves the quality of the seminal fluid (which becomes thicker as a result of this exercise) and helps them sublimate their sex urge. However, they add that, since this posture tones up the sexual organs, a regular practitioner of this posture, if he happens to be a man of the world 'interested in legitimate progeny', will find this posture very effective in improving his sexual performance. It is believed that children whose parents performed this exercise regularly are strong, healthy and intelligent. This posture prevents and cures stiffness of body resulting from old age. Along with the whole series of Gorakshasanas it is said to lead to the removal of the stiffness of joints (particularly of the knees and ankles), oedema and swelling of the feet, premature ejaculation, lax erections and wet dreams. It strengthens the inguinal and hamstring muscles and affords prophylaxis to those with a tendency to hernia. It also strengthens the circulatory and neuro-muscular system of the female urogenital organs and improves the chances of conception. A regular practice of this Asana is strongly recommended for both men and women.

Goraksha Pose 2

Posture 🏃
Sit in Goraksha Pose 1, and without moving the position of the joined feet place both hands on the ground in front of your knees. Raise your body on your hands and swing your hips forward and deposit them on your heels, so that you sit on your heels instead of on the ground with the inner side of your heels forming your seat. Having firmly seated yourself on your feet, raise your hands from the ground and place them on your knees (Plate 8B). Hold this posture for a minimum of ten seconds. Keep your eyes open. Continue deep breathing.

Benefits 🏃
The benefits of this posture are the same as those of Goraksha Pose 1 except that they are much more pronounced. Those of you who are short of time can select this posture from among the six Goraksha Poses for your regular practice as it is much superior to the earlier one and much easier than the next four poses in this category.

69

9A
Goraksha Pose 3 (Bhagasana—Vulvar Pose)

Posture

Sit as in Goraksha Pose 1, and keeping the toes on the ground raise the heels upwards and outwards, still keeping the soles joined together. In the completed pose the feet will be supported on the ground by their toes only while the joined heels will be touching your pubic region (Plate 9A). Some Yogis, in their writings, have named this pose 'Bhagasana', a reference to the external appearance of the female genitals which is resembled by the ellipse formed by the hollows of the soles of the feet. It is enough for our purpose, however, to remember the pose as Goraksha Pose 3.

Benefits

The same as in Goraksha Pose 1.

Goraksha Pose 4 (Guhyapadasana—Hidden Feet Pose)

Posture 🏃

Sit down in Sukhasana (Plate 1A), then placing your hands on the ground on both sides of your body raise your hips from the ground and draw both your feet under your hips, placing one foot on the other as shown in Plate 9B, and sit down on your feet instead of on the ground. In this position, one foot will be on the ground with the other resting on it and the hips on top of the second foot. Then raise your hands from the ground and place them on your knees as you do in the Padmasana (Plate 1B). Hold this pose while you complete ten Yogic breaths (see Plate 31).

Repeat the pose after changing the position of the feet so that the lower foot is placed on the upper in the second half of the exercise.

Benefits 🏃

Apart from strengthening the bones, muscles, arteries and nerves of the ankles and the feet, this Asana improves the circulation of the neuro-muscular system serving the rectum, the perineum and the genitals. It strengthens the muscles and the nerves connected with the sex act. Consistent with the prin-ciple that flabby and weak sexual parts contri-bute to a greater craving for the sexual act, however ineffective they may be in performing it, the toning up of the sex centres by this Asana enables the Yogi to practise celibacy effectively. At the same time, it greatly improves the func-tioning of the sex organs in the case of those who are not interested in celibacy. Thus it is one of those Asanas which develop the individual's capa-city to direct his libido either towards sublimation or to-wards sexual functioning at will.

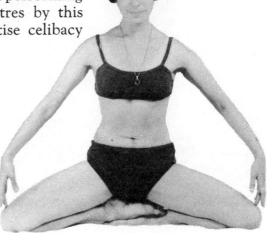

71

10A
Goraksha Pose 5

Posture 🕉

Sit in Goraksha Pose 3 as shown on the previous page. Then place your hands on the ground in front of you to enable you to raise your hips sufficiently above the ground to be able to turn the joined toes of your feet inwards underneath you so that you can sit on your feet with your joined heels pointing outwards in front of you. The inner sides of your feet are touching the ground and you are sitting on their outer edges. (See Plate 10A.) You will be able to understand the mechanics of this posture only if you keep Goraksha Pose 3 in your mind, and start turning your heels towards the ground in front of you and the toes inwards to go under your seat. This is a difficult posture and only those among you who are very keen to master all the poses and can afford to give sufficient time to the practice of the posture should attempt it. It could not possibly be omitted from a book which is expected to describe the important stages which constitute an aid to the development of an individual's sexual prowess but you can reap adequate benefits from the practice of the first and the second poses of the Goraksha series without taking to the practice of its more difficult postures.

Benefits 🕉
The same as in Goraksha Pose 2.

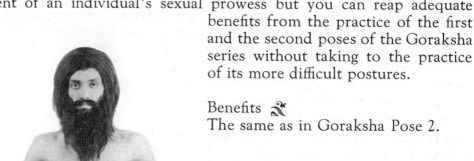

Posture 🏃

Sitting in Goraksha Pose 1, hold both your feet, which are firmly on the ground on their outer edges, with both your hands and bend your trunk forward without raising your hips from the ground till your nose and chin touch the ground. Hold yourself in this pose for five to ten seconds or even less, to begin with. You can raise this period to fifteen or thirty seconds when you have acquired adequate flexibility to practise this pose with comparative ease. Keep your eyes open and continue slow and deep breathing (Plate 10B).

Benefits 🏃

The same as described in Goraksha Pose 5. It gives an added advantage of exercising your alimentary canal and stretching your spine, thereby improving the functioning of both these important areas.

11
Vistrita Padasana—Lateral Stretched Legs Pose

Posture 🦂
Sit down on the ground with both your legs stretched out to your right and your left respectively so that both the legs form one straight line. Keep your hands on your legs as shown in Plate 11. Keep the eyes open, body erect, legs straight and muscles relaxed to the greatest extent possible. Continue deep and slow breathing.

Benefits

This Asana improves the tone of the circulatory and neuro-muscular systems of the entire pelvis including the organs of reproduction and elimination. It cures cramps of the lower extremities and strengthens the muscles and the ligaments of the calves, the thighs and all the joints of the legs. It tends to increase the height if the exercise is done regularly and for a long time. It tones up the sex centres of the body both for purposes of sublimation of the sex urge in the case of the recluse and the ascetic and improvement of sexual efficiency in the case of the normal individual.

12
Janushirasana—Knee—Head Pose 1

Posture 🏃

Sit down on the ground with your left leg stretched out straight before you and the right leg bent inwards at the knee so that the right heel is in touch with your body and if possible touching your perineum. Then, bending forward, hold the big toe of your left foot with the thumb and two adjacent fingers of both hands. In this process, the left leg should be kept absolutely straight without permitting any bending of the left knee. Bend forward further to bring your forehead into contact with your knee. The right knee also should be kept in contact with the ground. The eyes can be kept closed or open. Continue deep breathing.

Repeat the posture with the right leg stretched out and the left foot near the perineum, the rest of the posture remaining the same. The forehead in the latter posture will touch the right knee instead of the left knee.

Persons with bulging abdomens or stiff backs or joints will find it difficult to bring their foreheads into contact with their knees and they will find their knees rising from the ground to touch the forehead. Such a compromise is permissible for beginners. For the first few days there is a possibility of the exerciser experiencing some pain in the parts

exercised by this posture. This should not result in giving up the practice of this posture. The exercise should be continued in an imperfect manner, but regularly and daily.

Benefits ℘
This exercise improves the circulation and tones up the neuro-muscular system of the perineum and the gonads. Yogis prescribe it for spermatorrhoea, wet dreams and night emissions, defects in semen, and other sexual disorders. It also tones up the liver and the muscles and ligaments of the ribs and both sides of the trunk. It strengthens the urinary bladder and seminal vesicles. It is also prescribed for stones in the kidneys, urethra and bladder. It is often prescribed for women to tone up the muscles of the uterus, the fallopian tubes and to improve the functioning of the ovaries. Practised regularly by healthy couples, it will improve their sexual tone and performance.

13
Janushirasana—Knee—Head Pose 2

Posture
Sit down on the ground with your left leg stretched out in front of you
and the right leg bent inwards at the knee so that the right heel is in
touch with your left thigh. Then hold your right ankle with your hands,
raise your foot and place it on your left thigh instead of leaving it on the
ground touching your perineum as was done in the previous pose,
Janushirasana No. 1. The rest of the posture is exactly the same as
Janushirasana No. 1—i.e., hold the big toe of your left foot with both

hands using the thumbs and two adjacent fingers and bend down to bring your forehead into contact with your left knee.

Repeat the posture with the right leg stretched out and the left foot on the right thigh; the forehead in the reverse posture touching the right knee instead of the left knee.

Benefits ॐ
The same as in Janushirasana No. 1.

14
Janushirasana—Knee—Head Pose 3

Posture

Sit down on the ground and stretch the right leg in front of you, bend the left leg inwards at the knee and place your left heel on the right thigh as in the reverse position of Janushirasana No. 2. Now bend forward and use only your right hand to hold the big toe of your right foot while your forehead touches the right knee and your left arm goes behind across your back to hold the big toe of your left foot which is resting on the right thigh (Plate 14A).

Reverse the pose with the left leg stretched, the right foot on the left knee, the forehead on the left knee and left hand holding the big toe of the left leg, the right hand going behind across the back to hold the big toe of the right foot (Plate 14B). Continue deep breathing as in the previous two poses.

Benefits

The benefits of the Janushirasana No. 3 are the same as from the previous two poses of this Asana except that they are more pronounced. If you find it difficult to practise this pose, it can be abandoned in favour of the previous two Asanas which are quite adequate in conferring the benefits enumerated in Janushirasana No. 1.

15
Veerya Stambhanasana—Semen Retention Pose

Posture ⚐

Stand on the ground with one foot behind and one foot forward maintaining a distance of approximately one long stride between them. Then start bending the knee of the forward leg till the upper half of the leg is at right angles to the lower half and the latter is at right angles to the ground. While doing so, hold your hands behind your back as shown in Plate 15 and, keeping your back straight, bring your head down so that your nose touches the large toe of your leading foot. The leg behind should not be allowed to bend in this process. Hold yourself in this pose for half to one minute. Then rise slowly and disengage yourself from the pose. Repeat the posture reversing the position of the legs.

While disengaging from the pose, fill the lungs fully and then stand erect. The body should be kept immobile during the pose. The breath should be held in the lungs after full inhalation so that the chest remains a little thrown out and the abdomen drawn inwards. This posture is deemed to have been completed only after it has been done with both feet in the forward position. This Asana has also been called Padangushtha Nasa Sparshanasana.

Benefits
The benefits of this posture are similar to those of Bhadrasana and Gorakshasana. Yogic experts are unanimous in their praise of this Asana as being very effective in toning up the sex centres. It is therefore practised both by the recluse for the effective sublimation of the sex urge and by the family man for the strengthening of the sex centres for better sexual performance. It promotes and prolongs youth and post-pones and delays old age. It counters the effects of sexual excesses. It is supposed to cure borderline diabetes and to help bring the sugar levels in advanced diabetes towards the normal even when the drop in the level is not adequate.

Those of you who have a tendency to diabetes but have not started suffering from it yet, and also happen to have a sweet tooth, should perform it regularly. The pose also tends to control morbid, excessive sexual desires bordering on mania and helps counter the deleterious effects of sexual excesses. It is claimed that it cures mild glycosuria (sugar in the urine) resulting from excessive intake of food promoting tendency to diabetes. It is considered the best Asana for the cure of premature ejaculation and the thinness of seminal fluid. The regular practitioners of this Asana will notice that it thickens the consistency of the seminal fluid. It cures insomnia, anaemia, flatulence, abdominal pains, tendency to inguinal hernia. In general it improves the tone of the entire body and is equally beneficial for the male and the female.

16
Eka Pada Shirasana—Foot–Head Pose

Posture 🕉

Sit on the ground with the left leg stretched in front of you and lift your right foot with both your hands, bend your head and carry the foot over your head and place it on your neck (Plate 16A). Then straighten your back and fold both your hands in front of your chest as is done in Indian salutation. Keep the head also erect. Continue normal deep breathing. Keep the eyes open. Don't relax the body in this pose.

Repeat the same pose in reverse—i.e., with the right leg stretched and the left foot on the neck, the rest of the pose remaining the same (Plate 16B).

Benefits &

Yogis prescribe this Asana for women who suffer from prolapse of the uterus, laxity of urogenital musculature and tendency to miscarriage and abortion. It is also prescribed, with good results, for piles. It tones up the male and female gonads and reduces minor swellings of the scrotum by improving the blood circulation. It reduces oedema in the extremities. It also tones up the respiratory tract and improves appetite. It improves the flexibility of the muscles of the legs, the back and the waist.

17
Dvipada Shirasana—Feet–Head Pose

Posture

Sit on the ground in the foot-head posture. Bend forward and lift the remaining foot off the ground with both your hands and bring it over your head to be placed on the back so that both feet are now behind your neck. Fold both your hands as you did in the previous posture. In a variant of this pose, place your palms on the ground either side of your body and, supporting your entire weight on your hands, raise yourself from the ground (as in the Swing Pose that follows next) without disturbing the position of your head and legs, as shown in the plates.

Benefits

This posture confers the same benefits, in a greater degree, as those derived from the foot-head posture. It strengthens the spinal column and the shoulders. The calves and feet are strengthened. It improves the flexibility of the entire body and cures the stiffness of muscles in general. It improves physical efficiency and imparts great flexibility to the entire system. It also tones up the kidneys and promotes easier and more effective evacuation of the bladder and the bowels.

18A
Lolasana—Swing Pose 1

Posture 🕉

Sit in Padmasana (Lotus Pose), then place your palms on the ground on both sides of your body and, supporting your entire weight on your hands, raise the remaining part of the body from the ground keeping the Lotus Pose intact. Fill the lungs with a deep breath before lifting the body from the ground. Keeping the eyes open, take five deep breaths in this pose before gradually letting the body down to the ground, filling the lungs with a deep breath as you do so. Keep the abdomen contracted and the chest expanded during this exercise. Keep the body as steady as possible during the posture. If it is difficult to hold the body above the ground for the duration of five full deep breaths, you can terminate the pose earlier.

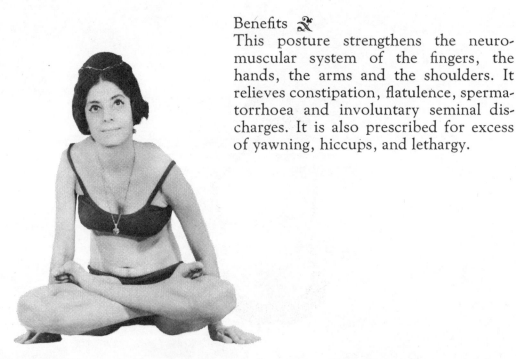

Benefits 🕉

This posture strengthens the neuro-muscular system of the fingers, the hands, the arms and the shoulders. It relieves constipation, flatulence, spermatorrhoea and involuntary seminal discharges. It is also prescribed for excess of yawning, hiccups, and lethargy.

18B
Lolasana—Swing Pose 2

Posture
Another variety of Lolasana (Swing Pose) is raising the body still higher so that the knees rest against the arms above the elbows and the trunk is at right angles to the arms (Plate 18B).

Benefits
The benefits are identical with those of the first variety of Lolasana.

19
Garbhasana—Foetus Pose

Posture

Sit on the ground with both hands resting on the ground in front of you with a distance of about one foot between them. Bring your right leg around the right arm so that the arm is placed between the inner side of the calf and the thigh touching the inner side of the knee joint. Similarly, the left arm should be embraced by the inner side of the left knee joint. Keeping the arms in position, bring in the right foot behind the left arm and the left foot behind the right arm. The position of the two feet now resembles, to some extent, that of the two feet in Padmasana (Lotus Pose) except that now your arms are inside the respective folds of your legs instead of outside them as in the Padmasana. Now raise your forearms and holding the lower portion of your calves in the inner folds of your elbows, raise your hands and place them on both sides of your face. This will automatically raise your feet to the level of your abdomen against which they will be held by the folds of your elbows. Hold the pose from five to fifteen seconds, keep the eyes open, continue to breathe comfortably, hold the body firmly during the pose, keep the head as straight as possible. If it is found difficult to hold the body in balance, through fear of toppling backwards, the Asana may be performed with the back supported against a wall. As confidence develops with the progress of the exercise, the support of the wall should be given up.

Benefits

This posture is named the Foetus Pose due to its partial resemblance to the position of the foetus in the womb. The Yogis also claim that this posture imparts the same softness and flexibility to the body as is possessed by the tissues of the foetus in the womb. It is supposed to confer a large number of benefits, the most surprising being relief in cases of granular pharyngitis and also of granulation on the back portion of the tongue. It is also prescribed for stomatitis, inflammatory conditions in general of the buccal cavity and the lips, pimples on the face, and poor complexion. It imparts considerable relief in cases of colitis. It tones up the organs of digestion and cures flatulence. It is also beneficial in cases of dysmenorrhoea. It tones up urogenital organs and cures impurities in urine. This is one of those postures which is freely prescribed for all, from childhood to ripe old age, and for both sexes.

20
Shirshasana— Head Stand

Posture 🦎

Spread a soft blanket or a thin foam-rubber mattress on the ground. Squat in the middle of the blanket. Interlocking the fingers of both hands in front of you with the palms facing towards you, bend slowly forward and place the interlocked hands on the ground in front of you keeping both palms open to support the back part of your head which you place on the ground. Then, gradually tilt your body upwards so that the weight of your body is borne by your head supported by the interlocked hands behind and the forearms in the front. The elbows and the head form a supporting triangle enabling you to stand straight on your head. Hold the pose for one or two minutes. Beginners may practise the pose for fifteen to thirty seconds. Breathing should be normal.

If you cannot hold yourself erect whilst standing on your head, use the support of a wall. The benefit will be practically the same. Squat in front of the wall, place your hands on the ground (at a convenient distance from the wall) so that they form a triangle with your head when you place it on the ground against the wall (using a towel for protection). Using your hands to bear the weight of your body, raise your heels and legs, tilting them backwards and upwards, so that they go up and touch the wall. Hold your body straight against the wall with the heels and the back of the head touching the wall. In this position you cannot fall on any side as you have the support of your hands at the front and the sides and of the wall at your back.

Benefits 🦎

The Head Stand has become popular in present-day Yoga in spite of the fact that no direct reference to it is to be found in any of the classical Yoga texts.

This pose improves the blood supply to the brain and the adjoining portion of the spinal cord. The practice of this Asana improves eye-sight, hearing and the sense of smell. It tones up the vocal cords and improves the voice. It promotes sound sleep. Normally those who practise it can gain more benefit during a sleep session of four hours than others in eight hours. The vascular system serving the brain and its nerves is exercised and strengthened by this posture and thereby feeding and serving the entire cerebral area with greater efficiency. It improves concentration and induces serenity and tranquillity.

It tends to reduce funk and anxiety conditions and can therefore contribute to the cure of psychic sex disturbances. It is also supposed to make the greatest contribution of all the Asanas to intelligence and enthusiasm.

IMPORTANT: Shirshasana should be immediately followed by Shavasana (Pose of Tranquillity) the duration of which should be equal to the duration of time given to Shirshasana. This is a must. The exerciser should not stand erect after the Shirsha-sana before completing the Shavasana which should follow it immediately. This Shavasana is normally practised at the end of all the exercises but in this case it should be done both after the Head Stand and as the last exercise of all.

It is essential that the stomach should be empty when practis-ing Shirshasana. People with a tendency to nose bleeds and high blood pressure should avoid it. However, people who have only a mildly high blood pressure can safely perform it and even derive benefit from it. It should not be performed when the body is heated by other exercises. Other people who should avoid the Head Stand are those suffering from chronic and advanced asthma, tuberculosis, cancer, septic and inflammatory diseases of ear, nose and throat, headaches, obesity and hyper-acidity. Even in these conditions, this posture has been tried by enthusiasts, but only under the guidance of physicians fully conversant with the theory and practice of Yoga.

21A
Utthitapadasana—Raised Legs Pose

Posture 🏃

Lie on the ground on your back with the entire body stretched at full length. The palms of the hands should be touching your thighs on both sides and the feet should be held together. Then raise your legs high so that they form an angle of approximately forty-five degrees with the ground. This is Utthitapadasana or Raised Legs Pose (Plate 21A). Hold this pose for one to fifteen seconds. Then, without lowering the legs, raise the head, shoulders and back so that from the feet to the head the body forms a concave figure with the hips and the waist touching the ground (Plate 21B). Hold yourself in this position for half to one minute. Continue deep breathing. Finally, take a deep breath and bring back the feet and the head to the ground to terminate the pose.

Utthitapadashirasana—Raised Head and Legs Pose

Benefits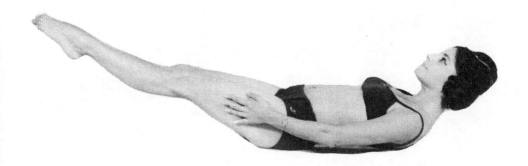

These two postures improve the tone of the intestinal and abdominal muscles. When certain intestinal disorders such as pain, griping, diarrhoea, etc., resist modern or traditional treatment, Yogis sometimes attribute them to 'displacement of navel', and manipulation of the area around the navel for removal of this displacement often brings spectacular relief to the patients after the failure of the best of medical treatment. These postures counter the tendency to 'displacement of navel' and disorders arising therefrom. They tone up the digestive apparatus and also exercise a beneficial effect on the blood-vascular and neuro-muscular systems of the pubic regions.

22
Chakrasana—Wheel Pose

Posture ⚹

Lie down on your back, draw up the knees so that they point upwards while the heel of each foot touches the corresponding hip with the soles of the feet resting on the ground. Place your hands on either side of your head with the elbows pointing upwards and the palms and the fingers resting squarely on the ground. Then supporting the weight of your body on your hands and feet raise your hips and abdomen as high as you can so that the entire body describes an arch with only the hands and the feet touching the ground. Keep the body as still as possible. The hands and feet should hold the ground and remain firmly in position. Raise the back as far up as possible so that the body imitates the shape of the rim of a wheel as much as possible. Take a deep breath before raising the body. Continue deep breathing during the posture. Fill the lungs again with air before slowly returning to the ground at the end of the exercise. After lying down on the ground, deep breathing should continue for a few seconds. The eyes may be open or closed.

Benefits

This posture keeps the spine young and flexible even during old age. It helps the exerciser retain the flexibility and lightness of all the dorsal and ventral muscles. The Yogis prescribe this posture for improving the eyesight, and the richness and clarity of the voice. It is also claimed that it tones up the lymph glands and clears inflammatory conditions. It improves the texture and complexion of the skin. It tones up the sex centre in the spine. It also gives relief in cases of constipation, flatulence, nausea and asthma. It is claimed that it removes unpleasant sensations (pins and needles, burning, tenderness, pricking, general debility, rigidity, and anorexia, or lack of appetite). It tones up the nerves serving the organs of sight, hearing, smell and taste. It also improves the circulation of blood to the brain, thereby contributing to intelligence and alertness. It stretches and tones up the inguinal and pelvic muscles and vessels and tones up the pelvic organs.

23
Eka Pada Shalabhasana—Locust Pose 1

Posture ॐ
Lie down flat and full length on your abdomen with both arms resting
on the ground, close to your body. The chin should also be touching
the ground. The upper surface of the stretched feet should also be in
contact with the ground. Then take a deep breath and raise the left leg
from the hip as far above the ground as you can, avoiding too much
difficulty or distress. Then slowly exhale and take five deep breaths.
Again fill your lungs with a deep breath and slowly bring down the leg
to the original position on the ground. Repeat the entire process with
the right leg. Do not bend your knees during the exercise and remember
to keep the leg in a straight line with the body.

Benefits

The Locust Pose tones up the male gonads and the female pelvic viscera, thereby improving the general tone of the tissues connected with sexual and urogenital functions. It streamlines and dissolves fat from the knees, hips, waist and abdomen. It tones up the muscles of the dorsal, lumbar and sacral spine. It counters tendency to constipation and piles. It improves the circulation of the large intestines and removes flatulence. It also removes the aches and pains of the areas referred to above. Yoga teachers particularly recommend this posture for practice by women.

24
Dvipada Shalabhasana—Locust Pose 2

Posture

Lie down on the ground face downwards as in Pose 1. In both Poses 1 and 2 the arms and hands should be on the ground, the entire length of the arm touching the body right up to the sides of the thighs. Fill the lungs with a deep breath, raise both the legs upwards as far as you can take them without experiencing too much discomfort or distress. Take three to five deep breaths in that position. Again fill the lungs with a deep breath and slowly bring the legs down till they rest on the ground. Do not bend the knees and throughout the exercise keep both the legs straight; the legs should not separate. The chin should remain in touch with the ground. The exerciser will not be able to raise the legs very far from the ground. Only through long practice will the requisite flexibility to practise the posture efficiently be acquired.

Benefits 🏃

This posture tones up the ligaments, tendons, muscles, and nerves of the lower back and the waist in general. It improves the circulation of the entire pelvic region, toning up all the organs and viscera of the area including the gonads. It tones up the entire urogenital apparatus. It reduces oedema of the ankles and feet. It is beneficial for women suffering from dysmenorrhoea and irregular periods. It is also helpful in alleviating piles. Yoga teachers also prescribe this Asana to patients for relief of painful urination, diabetes, and scanty urine as a further aid to the treatment they may be undergoing.

25
Urdhwa Sarvangasana—Shoulder Stand Pose

Posture 𝒮

Lie on your back full length, legs together and arms touching your sides. Raise your legs and trunk so that the entire weight of the raised legs and trunk is borne by the shoulders. The elbows should be resting on the ground with both hands and the forearms supporting the back to keep the body erect and in position for the posture. From the tip of the toes down to the shoulders the entire body should be in a straight line and at right angles to the ground. The chin should be pressing against the lower part of the neck. The elbows should be neither too far from the body nor too near it. Try to extend the feet and the toes upwards as much as possible. Do not bend the knees and keep still though relaxed. Fix your gaze on your toes. If this results in the eyes watering, close them and relax. Breathing during this posture should continue to be deep and slow.

It may not be possible for obese people to perform this Asana to perfection. Probably they will be able to raise only their legs and not the trunk. This should not discourage them. They should raise their legs as far as they can without feeling much discomfort and distress.

Benefits ॐ

The Yogic classification enumerates ten *indriyas* or organs of perception and action. The organs of sense are those of touch, taste, sight, hearing and smell. The organs of action are the hands and feet, the two excretory organs of urination and defecation and the organ of speech. This pose is considered to improve the action of all of them. It also improves the functioning of the cervical (neck) vessels and vocal cords and will improve a singer's voice. Experiments have confirmed that it improves the functioning .of the liver and digestive system, and tones up the nerves and musculature of the head and the trunk. It is a prophylactic against many diseases. Yogis attach great importance to this posture as an aid to the awakening of the Kundalini, the mysterious power capable of leading the Sadhaka (Aspirant) to Absolute Perfection. But even for normal people, men and women alike, it is a highly beneficial posture conferring practically all the benefits that the head-stand bestows, without any of the possible harmful side-effects.

26
Halasana—Plough Pose

Posture

Lie down on the ground on your back, raise the legs upwards, then raise the back with the help of both hands until you attain the Urdhwa Sarvangasana (Shoulder Stand—Plate 25). Then tilt your legs slowly until your toes touch the ground behind your head. Keep your legs straight and do not bend the knees. Then stretch your arms behind your back so that they rest in the opposite direction to the legs, lying parallel to each other with the palms touching the ground. The body now rests on the shoulders, neck and head, the pose resembling a plough. Keep the eyes open. If you cannot continue deep breathing in this posture you can breathe normally while holding this pose.

Benefits ❧

This Asana is also known as Sarvangasana which literally means 'all-parts posture'. It exercises and stretches the posterior muscles of the entire body. It improves the circulation and tone of the whole length of the spinal cord, and at the same time benefits the arms and legs. It tones up the thyroid gland. It imparts elasticity and pliability to the spinal cord, 'oiling' the roots of the bilateral nerve branches of the spinal cord (thirty-two pairs in all, serving the major part of the body). The stretching involved in this exercise enlarges the passages (vertebral foramina) through which the branches of the spinal cord pass out into the body, thereby raising considerably—and sometimes spectacularly—the efficiency and performance of the entire spinal nervous system and the areas served by it. Its regular practice improves the functioning of the thoracic and abdominal viscera in general. It improves the circulation of the brain, thereby contributing to intelligence, alertness and good memory.

Halasana also tones up the entire pelvic region and activates the gonadal secretions in the male and the female. It exercises the neuro-musculo-circulatory systems and the tissues surrounding and adjoining the sex centres in the spine, thereby substantially improving the sexual efficiency of the individual.

27A
Matsyasana—Crocodile Pose 1 (With Back and Head on Ground)

Posture ✗

First, sit in the Lotus Pose (Padmasana), then gradually bend backwards until you are lying on your back with the legs still fixed in the Lotus posture (Plate 27A). Flex your head backwards and arch your back by raising your chest and abdomen so that the entire body rests on the knees and the head. The head should be stretched backwards so that the highest point of the head is resting on the ground (Plate 27B). Breathe slowly and deeply, feeling relaxed.

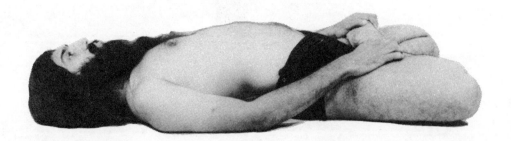

27B
Matsyasana—Crocodile Pose 2 (With Back and Head Stretched)

Benefits

This posture relieves constipation and tones up all the areas of the spine, including the sex centre. It is said to be particularly beneficial to women as it normalizes uterine functioning.

It tones up the lungs and muscles of the chest. It improves the circulation of the throat and tends to reduce tonsils. It is said that those who practise this posture regularly maintain a strong and erect spine even during old age. Even if one has developed a slight stoop, regular practice of this posture will help to correct it. It is also said to help diabetics by improving their general metabolism. People suffering from spinal pain should practise it regularly. There is no harm in practising it in part if you are unable to achieve the perfect posture. Even while practising an imperfect posture, the exerciser should keep his mind and body free from tension and rigidity. If it is not possible to eliminate tension completely, it should be reduced to the minimum.

28
Bhujangasana—Serpent Pose

Posture

Lie down full length face downwards; then, placing both your hands on the ground alongside your shoulders, raise your chest on your arms as high as you can with your head stretched backwards. The body from the waist down to the toes should remain in touch with the ground, the legs and the feet being held together. Breathe slowly and deeply.

Benefits ☀

This is an excellent pose for reducing abdominal fat and relieving constipation and flatulence. Its contribution to relief from spinal pain is remarkable considering the simplicity of the pose. If practised patiently and diligently it helps the exerciser to get over spinal pain of long standing, even when caused by osteo-arthritic changes in the spine. Its benefits affect the entire length of the vertebral column, including the cervical, the thoracic, the dorsal, and the sacral vertebrae, and the coccyx (these words denote the divisions of the spine into the neck, the upper back, the middle back, the lower back, and the tailbone respectively). It also tones up the muscles, tendons, and ligaments, the nerves and the blood vessels of the spinal region.

Since this pose exercises the spinal sex centre, it makes a substantial contribution to the effectiveness of the sexual performance of both men and women.

29
Dhanurasana—Bow Pose

Posture

Lie down on your chest and abdomen with your arms resting alongside your body. Throughout the exercise both the legs and the feet should remain joined together. Lift both the feet and legs upwards and backwards, bringing them towards your head until, with your arms raised behind you, you can hold both the ankles, the left ankle in the left hand and the right ankle in the right hand. The head should be held high. The chest also should be raised from the ground so that only the abdomen and the pelvis remain in contact with the ground. The pose should be held steady without any movement except that of the respiratory tract. Fill the lungs with air before raising the legs and the chest. At the completion of the pose continue normal breathing if deep breathing appears to be difficult. The feet may tend to come down towards the waist, but if you remain firm in your pose you can hold them steady. Keep the eyes open. Fill the lungs when returning to the ground to terminate the pose.

When you are accustomed to this posture learn to rock backwards and forwards (like a rocking chair).

Benefits

This posture exercises the entire body. It strengthens the deep and the superficial muscles of the entire spine, removing rigidity, stiffness, aches, pains, burning sensations, and tenderness of the spine and areas adjacent to it and served by the branches of the spinal cord. It also strengthens the spinal sex centre and both the male and female gonads, thereby improving the sexual performance. It tones up and develops the muscles of the chest. It improves the function of the liver, the kidneys, the bladder, the genital organs and other pelvic and abdominal viscera. It is a prophylactic against the formation of stones in the kidney and gall bladder. It relieves scanty, painful and burning urination. Practised regularly in middle age, it is believed to have a healthy effect on the prostate gland and to protect against enlargement or inflammation of this gland. It gives relief against piles, anorexia (dislike for food), flatulence, and halitosis (bad breath) when not caused by pyorrhoea. This Asana should not be performed by anyone suffering from a slipped disc.

30
Merusankarshasana—Spinal Traction Pose

Posture 👶

Lie down on a hard bed or table on your back with your body stretched full length but with the entire neck and head hanging beyond the edge of the bed, so that the full weight of the head is subjected to the gravitational pull of the earth without any support whatsoever. Relax the entire body as much as you can so that the relaxed muscles of the neck do not interfere with the full force of gravity pulling the head downwards. In this way the maximum weight of the head will exert a tractional pull on the entire spine and tend to increase the inter-vertebral spaces. Lie thus for five minutes, then, retaining the same position, flex your feet, with heels firmly held against the surface of the bed, towards your face in an effort to bring the toes of your feet into contact with your legs. This will exercise another strong pull on the back muscles of the body all along the line. Then slowly extend the feet in the opposite direction in an attempt to touch the surface of the bed with your toes. Of course, you can neither touch your legs nor the bed with your toes but try to cover the maximum distance in arching your feet on both sides. The movement should be slow and rhythmical and the pull in either direction the fullest you can manage. At the extreme end of the pull on either side hold the feet in position for one second. Repeat the exercise ten times. Keep the head hanging over the edge of the bed during this exercise.

During all this period both your arms should be spread out at right angles to your body and slipped slightly beyond the sides of the bed so that they, too, are unsupported. This will stretch the shoulders outwards. At the end of the feet exercise described above, move the arms towards the head so that they are in a straight line with the whole body. Even in this position, the arms should be so relaxed that their full gravitational pull downwards is not reduced by any tension of the muscles. This will exercise an outward pull on the muscles of the chest. The novice may feel the stretch of the chest muscles uncomfortable after a few seconds. If it becomes too uncomfortable, the arms should be taken back to the horizontal position until the sensation of discomfort in the chest muscles subsides. After five minutes of this exercise slide down so that the head now rests on the bed and the legs hang over the opposite end of the bed. This exercises an automatic stretch on the pelvis (Plate 30B). After a few minutes slide your legs down so that your feet are on the floor and then sit up with the help of your hands on the bed. Keep sitting from half to one minute. This completes the exercise and you can then leave the bed. Plate 30A shows first of all the spinal traction caused by the gravitational pull on the head as well as by the feet exercise, and at the same time illustrates a form of the pelvic stretch caused by the legs hanging beyond the bed.

30A

Benefits ॐ

Orthopaedic surgeons usually treat spinal pains, sciatica, brachial neuralgia, pains in neck and shoulder blades, arising out of intervertebral pressure on spinal nerves, by subjecting the patients to traction by placing them in a horizontal position with their feet stretched outside the edge of the bed with weights tied to their ankles to exert a pull on the spine. Since the very concept of Yoga aims at using an individual's own body for meeting all its needs, the device of using the weight of the head in place of attaching extraneous weight to the feet not only fulfils this condition, but our experience has shown that its results are superior to those of the prevalent method of traction. The exercise brings about better and more speedy relief in all pains in which traction is indicated.

This posture has not so far been mentioned by any books, ancient or modern, to my knowledge. We started this experiment on some patients and found it very beneficial. The name is also our invention.

30B

31
Pranayama—Yogic Breathing

Pranayama should be performed after you have completed your routine of Asanas. Sit erect but relaxed in the Lotus Pose (Padmasana). If you do not feel comfortable and cannot relax in this pose, adopt the Easy Pose (Sukhasana). Sitting in this pose, complete a series of twenty-five 4-unit Yogic breaths in the following order:

Right nostril breathing: Close the left nostril with the little finger of your right hand and take five Yogic breaths with your right nostril—i.e., inhale (Puraka), pause (Kumbhaka), exhale (Rechaka), and pause (Shunyaka). Repeat four more times.

Left nostril breathing: Now release the left nostril and close the right nostril with your right thumb. Take five 4-unit Yogic breaths through your left nostril.

Alternate breathing 1: Inhale (Puraka) through the right nostril, keeping the left nostril closed with the little finger, pause (Kumbhaka), then close the right nostril with the right thumb and exhale through the left nostril (Rechaka), and pause (Shunyaka). Repeat four more times (Fig. 10).

Fig. 10 Position of right hand for closing left nostril with the little finger and right nostril with the thumb.

116

Alternate breathing 2: Repeat *Alternate breathing 1* in reverse.

Simultaneous bilateral breathing: Take five full 4-unit Yogic breaths with both nostrils open. While doing so, the backs of both your hands should be resting on your knees with the tips of the thumb and the index finger of each hand meeting together to form a circle between the two, the other three fingers of each hand remaining fully stretched.

Kapala-Bhati (Bellows breathing): The above-mentioned twenty-five Pranayamic breaths should be followed by ten quick deep breaths without any pauses between inhalations and exhalations or exhalations and inhalations. The posture for bellows breathing, so called because the sound of powerful breaths taken in quick succession resembles that of air being pushed out from bellows, has to be the same as for practising Pranayama, except that it is the palms of the hands that rest on the knees in the case of this type of breathing. Ordinarily, ten such forceful and quick breaths suffice as an adequate exercise of the lungs and the nasal passages for an average person. It is one of the most effective exercises to remove difficulty in breathing due to blocked nasal passages when the blocking does not result from polypi or tumours. The practice considerably enhances the efficiency of the respiratory system.

117

32
Shavasana—Pose of Tranquillity

Posture 🏃

Lie down on your back with both arms lying close to your body. Relax yourself completely so that if someone raises your arm or leg, it falls down as if there were no life in it. No part of the body should make the slightest movement, and yet no tension should remain in any part of the body. Detach yourself completely from the problems of your life and if you have nothing better to concentrate upon, just give your entire attention to your breathing which should be deep, slow and easy.

At first glance, Shavasana appears to be the easiest of all Asanas to perform. A number of lazy people with blank minds tend to perform it unconsciously. Yet it is not so simple to achieve as it looks. In so far as one of the essential aspects of this Asana is total detachment of the mind from the happenings round about, entailing a deliberate cultivation of total blankness of mind, it is one of the most difficult postures to perform completely. One must learn to perfect this pose not only physically but also mentally as it is not possible to get the best out of this pose without a completely co-ordinated relaxation of the mind and the body.

Benefits 卐

This posture has been successfully utilized by eminent modern cardiologists in India to speed up the recovery of patients convalescing from heart diseases. It has been observed that patients practising Shavasana recover more quickly and completely. It also acts as a prophylactic against heart diseases in general. Practice of this posture helps to prevent the harmful effects on the body and mind of undue stress or anxiety, whether physical or mental. If one can achieve the right amount of detachment while relaxing in this pose, the feeling of relaxation will be far superior to that experienced from the use of tranquillizers and sedatives.

It need hardly be pointed out that the role of a truly relaxed psychosomatic system in achieving a rewarding sexual gratification and performance is very important.

Acknowledgments

The authors are grateful to:

Shri Hari Sharma, for supplying some valuable Sanskrit references;

Yogi Shri Umesh Chandra for offering the valuable services of his brilliant sons for posing for the photographs;

Dr N. U. Joshi, the handsome Yogi of this book;

Shri Sudarshan U. Joshi, who had to be brought in for the more difficult poses;

Miss Phiroza Lally, the beautiful ballet artiste, whose photographs adorn the pages of this book;

Miss Sophy Kelly, Principal, Hill Grange School, Bombay, for 'finding' Miss Lally for posing for the photographs;

Dr D. V. Bharati, Editor, *Dharma-yuga*, for kindly arranging the line drawings;

Mr Devendra Goel and Mrs Raj Goel of Goel Cine Corporation for lending the technical expertise of their capable executive, Mr Vijay Sadanah;

Mr Suhail of Hamilton Studio, Bombay, for the excellent photographs reproduced in this book;

Mr R. M. Sharma, for looking after the mobility and convenience of the participants in the production of the photographs;

Mr Ligorio Rodrigues, the brilliant stenographer, for his ungrudging hard work and exceptional devotion to duty.